The Gods and the Kings

The Gods and the Kings

A GLANCE AT CREATIVE POWER

JACQUES RUEFF

TRANSLATED BY *George Robinson*
AND *Roger Glémet*

Macmillan Publishing Co., Inc. • New York
Collier Macmillan Publishers • London

To all the scientists and all the thinkers without whom this book could not have been written

Jupiter: We're relatives: I made you in my image—a king is a god on earth. . . . We both make order reign, you in Argos, I in the world, and the same secret weighs heavy on our hearts.

Aegisthus: I haven't got any secret.

Jupiter: Yes you have—the same as mine. The sorry secret of gods and kings: that men are free. They are free, Aegisthus. You know it, but they do not.

Aegisthus: Good heavens, if they knew they'd burn down my palace. I've been doing all sorts of things for the past fifteen years to hide their power from them.

Jupiter: I've been at it for a hundred thousand years. Aegisthus, my brother and my creature, in the name of that order which we both serve, I command you: take Orestes into custody.

Aegisthus: Almighty God, why are you waiting to strike him down with a thunderbolt?

Jupiter: The gods have another secret, Aegisthus: Once freedom has burst out within a man, the gods can no longer do anything with him. . . .

SᴀʀᴛʀᴇT, The Flies, II, 5

Contents

Contents

Contents

The Discovery of Quanta Forces a New Interpretation of All Our Knowledge

ACCORDING TO Louis de Broglie, "the discovery of quanta, the consequences of which are only now beginning to become evident in all their scope, seems to require of scientific thought one of the greatest changes in orientation it has ever had to effect in its century-old effort to bring our idea of the physical world as closely as possible into line with the requirements of our reason."[1]

It was in connection with the theory of radiation that the concept of quanta, i.e. of discrete units, first forced itself upon the minds of physicists. From that field, it gradually spread to other areas of microscopic physics, with results that lead one to consider the idea that "physical reality consists of units which undergo successive transformations, involving sudden transitions. These transformations, however, cannot be described by means of infinitesimal analysis within the framework of continuity and determinism."[2]

The renovation thus effected in physics and related sciences

---

[1] Louis de Broglie, *Matter and Light*, 1939, p. 261.
[2] Ibid., p. 260.

has not yet even been attempted in other fields of knowledge, especially the human sciences. "In our day," says Eric Kraemer, ". . . it is almost as though centuries separated the quantum theory, which is the basis of the edifice of science in this atomic age, from the thought of economists and philosophers, marxists or technocrats. They no longer speak the same language. They no longer have a single idea in common."[3] It is across this chasm separating the two realms of the mind—sciences pledged to a strict interpretation of perceptible phenomena and those disciplines which have been unable or unwilling to learn from the facts—that this book attempts to throw a bridge.

First, we shall emphasize that the existence of quanta is a general phenomenon. The discovery of the existence of such individualities as fundamental particles, atoms, molecules, and living cells in the innermost substance of matter is a curious paradox. Instead, the discovery should have forced itself upon us in those areas where, since the individuals are of the same magnitude as ourselves, their presence could have been observed immediately: for example, in zoology, botany, political economy, or human sociology.

The next chapter will show that there is no reality in our universe which, when observed on an appropriate scale, does not appear as a conglomeration of associated individuals. This finding transforms all the natural sciences into "social sciences." Thus the study of integration processes—for example, those binding electrons and protons together within an atom, or living cells or organic groups of cells within an animal or a plant, or buyers and sellers in a market where bid and asking price have been matched—becomes the model of all scientific research.

Important knowledge can be gained by analyzing the characteristic social structures of our universe in terms of the processes by which they are established and maintained. This ap-

---

[3] Eric Kraemer, *La Grande Mutation.*

proach clarifies a number of problems which are obscure when they are considered in isolation. We shall see that—unlikely though this may seem—such a study of human societies can make an especially effective contribution to those cultures whose mechanisms are analyzed in terms of atomic and nuclear physics or biology. In this case, contrary to instances involving atoms, molecules, or biological substances, we do not directly perceive the existence of the society. However, introspection affords immediate knowledge of certain particulate processes, especially, of the interactions that affect or determine the behavior of those minute components made up of human persons. It is, then, the solemn advent of the "individual" in scientific thought that is being hailed in this book.

But I would not want anyone to do me the injustice of believing that I am systematically cultivating analogy. I am just as aware as anybody else that "comparisons are odious." Nor am I, on the other hand, unaware of the basic differences among the various orders of nature. Nevertheless, I am convinced that the similarities I shall attempt to unfold are neither coincidences nor flights of fancy; they are rather the necessary consequences of the social nature of all those structures which are the very fabric of our universe.

It has been extremely difficult for me to work out a way of presenting my reflections. To make my presentation complete or technical, I should have acquired a thorough command of the most recent discoveries of theoretical physics and biology. Being aware of my shortcomings in these fields, I have as often as possible cited the texts from which I gleaned my modest knowledge. I crave the reader's indulgence, in the hope that he will not accuse me of having assembled nothing more than a compilation, and I urge him to realize that my subject is so difficult and specialized that I could not run the risk of distorting, by summarizing or simply by abstracting, the texts whose substance had nurtured me. The opening chapters in particular include frequent quotations from Louis de Broglie. My book owes a great deal more to him, however, than mere references: without his works, especially *Matter and Light*, *Physique et microphysique*, and *Continu et discontinu en physique moderne*, it could never have been written.

Furthermore, a certain amount of apparent repetition will, I hope, also be condoned. It stems from a desire to impart unity to the various constituent parts of this book.

Many of my conclusions are more intuitions than demonstrations. It was this quality that, once before, prompted me to express them in a lyric play, with music filling any gaps of unfinished thought. But I soon grew weary of my characters and their irritating tendency to didacticism. So, to gain time, I resigned myself to the task of setting down my reflections in the frequently rough hewn form in which they had occurred to me. It is doubtless because of its theatrical origins that the chapter titles are somewhat less austere than one might expect in an investigation of creative power in the universe.

All in all, this book is only a pale reflection of the thoughts which have beset me since I began writing it. The subject I had in mind was probably too vast for me to encompass it with greater precision. With each new rough draft, I was always alive to the wisdom of Ernest Renan's remark, "If you want to be able to think freely you must rest assured that what you publish will not be of tremendous importance."[4]

I invite and accept beforehand the criticism of specialists and experts. But I hope their critical minds will stimulate them to make up for the inadequacy of my exposition, to correct and complete it, so that, with their help, this book will pave the way for the major synthesis which is about to emerge. Considering the present dispersion of human knowledge, this is an urgent and overriding necessity.

---

[4] *Dialogues philosophiques*, 2nd ed., 1876, p. x.

PART I

Introducing a Quantum
View of the Universe

CHAPTER I

Existence Is a Social State

Tнis снартеr is the cornerstone of the entire book. It stems from an essential observation: the particulate—physicists would say the quantified—character of *all* the reality we know.

The first two sections will show that, in our universe, existence is always gained by the formation of societies. The third section will establish, within the swarm of societies that make up the reality we know, essential hierarchical structures. Each society can be broken down into individuals of an immediately inferior rank, and each of those, in turn, forms a society for the elements which it encompasses.

The concept of pure continuity cannot yield an interpretation of reality in which individuals are to be discerned [1]

Most things around me—the air I breathe, the water I drink or wash in, my pen—look like continua to the naked eye. If science did not have at its disposal more penetrating means of

[1] Louis de Broglie, *Matter and Light*, p. 231.

observation, such as the electronic microscope, the universe would seem to be composed of homogeneous substances that are combined in various ways but always remain identical, no matter how they are broken down.

And yet, day by day, the advance of knowledge brings increasing evidence that such a concept cannot possibly yield the interpretation of the phenomena that more precise observation of perceptible appearances reveals.

The more experimenters have been refining their methods of investigation in the atomic and microscopic sphere, the more clearly it has appeared that the results of their experiments were most naturally expressed by the assumption that the structure of physical reality is discontinuous and comprises discrete units like the proton, the electron, and the photon. . . . Eventually, all the results of experimental microscopic Physics are now stated in corpuscular form.[2]

Where our fingers or our eyes have discerned only impenetrable matter or homogeneous fluid, scientific analysis has forced upon us a particulate representation according to which the observed phenomena have become the result of a very large number of simultaneous elementary activities.

The study of the properties of material bodies has led physicists to conclude that matter is formed of small corpuscles only, electrons and protons; various combinations of these corpuscles make up the atoms of the 92 simple bodies which are the bases of the molecules of the compound bodies. . . . the atom is a kind of miniature solar system, with the nucleus for its sun and the electrons for its planets, gravitating around a central, positively-charged sun.[3]

[2] Ibid., p. 257.
[3] Ibid., pp. 22, 71.

In the study of light, the particulate interpretation has also forced itself upon us: "It appeared that a certain number of facts were satisfactorily accounted for if it was assumed that light-energy was divided into corpuscles which have since been called photons." As to electricity, "experience . . . teaches us that negative electricity consists of minute corpuscles which are all identical, and have an extremely small mass and electric charge. These negative corpuscles are called electrons. . . . Positive electricity, too, is subdivided into corpuscles which are all identical which have been called protons."[4] These spheres of electricity are believed to constitute the substance of the atom.

Fundamental quantification,

> having first made its way into the theory of radiation, later invaded the whole field of physics. . . . In fact, the only corpuscular notion which is stable and is found in Nature is that which fulfills the condition that the mechanical action calculated for any complete period is equal to a multiple of Planck's constant h. Thus, this constant is found to play the part of a quantum of action. . . . Thus quanta found their way into mechanics, where they limit possible motion by rules of quantification, in which integers are operative. . . . The quantum of action has been found in a thousand phenomena. . . . Bohr's theory came later, to demonstrate that, if the atoms of matter are in a stable state, it is because of the character of the intra-atomic corpuscular movements. From then on, we have known that the stability of matter and its very existence rest on quanta. . . . The intervention of quanta brought about the generalized introduction of discontinuity in atomic physics.[5]

[4] Ibid., pp. 93, 21-22.
[5] Ibid., pp. 49–50, 35.

We are forced to similar conclusions as regards the lower forms of life: "In the lowest strata of life, there are viruses, bacteriophages, and mosaics, whose corpuscular nature, still doubtful twenty years ago, has now been confirmed by the electron microscope."[6] Progress in genetics has decisively confirmed the quantified nature of vital phenomena:

What transmits heredity is not a global representation of the organism, but a collection of discrete units governing its character. An individual's characteristics are fashioned out of a conglomeration of discontinuous units, just as a mosaic is made of small pieces of colored stone. . . . Thus the material of heredity may be resolved into elementary units: the genes become, as it were, the atoms of heredity. If a gene was able, through mutation, to have several discrete states, only one single such state would be represented in a chromosome. . . . Many biologists found it difficult to agree with the rigor and formalism of such a quantum view of heredity while they observed, day after day, some sort of continuity in variation. It was not at variance, however, with the concepts of physics, since biological qualities were reduced to indivisible units and their combinations were subject to the laws of probability which are governed by chance. We can no more predict the combination of certain genes in an individual than we can predict the motion of an isolated atom or electron. The only things we can measure or calculate are the distributions and probabilities relating to large populations.[7]

As pointed out in the Preamble, it is curious that the fundamental discontinuity of certain aspects of physical reality was recognized first and, until recently, exclusively in infinitely small things, where it cannot be perceived. It was not con-

[6] Ibid., p. 288.

[7] François Jacob, Nobel Prize Laureate, Inaugural Lecture at the College de France, May 7, 1965; printed in *Cahiers de l'Institut de la Vie*, no. 9, July 1966.

sciously apprehended in those areas—like the human sciences —whose isolated elements, i.e. the "individuals," can be observed directly apart from the global realm that is not perceptible to man.

Nevertheless, even in the first case we were long unaware of the existence of discontinuity except as a philosophical assumption, such as those made by Democritus and Leucippus. This was especially true because of the inability of our eyes and fingers, in the absence of any instrument capable of appropriate magnification, to discern and identify individual elementary particles; as a result, they could provide information about reality only in its global aspects.

The crystals in a steel ingot are beyond our immediate perception; we are aware only of the impenetrability of the solid. Similarly, whether in a liquid or a gas, or even in living matter, atoms, cells, or organs cannot be perceived by our senses alone. On the other hand, in a forest, if we do not stand far away, we can see only the trees. In a family, on a farm, in a factory or a city, we are aware of individuals, and of individuals only. Lastly, in the heavens, we see stars and planets separately; it is only in the Milky Way, which is so far away that we can encompass at a single glance the hundreds of billions of stars comprising it, that we view the substance of our galaxy as a continuum—like the milk from which it derives its name.

Continuity and discontinuity are not, therefore, intrinsic characteristics of the matter being observed, but the result of the size of the observer and the precision of his instruments relative to the size of the objects. In touching a liquid or a gas, for instance, our epidermis does not feel the successive impacts of the molecules. They are so frequent, and there are so many of them, relative to the segregating power of our skin, that we feel only pressure, the aggregate result of all the many molecular bombardments. Similarly, touch and sight cannot measure the speeds of individual molecules, although the temperature of the mass they constitute provides information about the aggregate variations at their mean square.

But just imagine the impression this universe would make on someone of molecular dimensions—someone in the same position in relation to other molecules as we are within human societies. He would "see" great empty spaces through which isolated molecules moved at different speeds, only rarely encountering one another. Those molecules would be his only "physical reality." He would be unaware of, and could not even directly observe, those correlations which humans express in the laws of gases.

Nonetheless, if this molecular observer could hold sufficiently aloof, he would be able to take a position, in relation to the molecules, similar to that of an econometricst observing human phenomena. Through a brilliant synthesis, he might discover the existence, on a level superior to his own, of macroscopic entities that are subject to constant laws. By drawing two boundary lines within the mass of gas which constitutes his universe, for instance, he could work out statistics for the speeds and masses of the molecules which moved across those lines. His search for correlation would reveal constant relations between the mean molecular speed and the volume of the container. These relations would represent a microscopic version, so to speak, of Mariotte's law, just as the constant relation between mean square speed and pressure would be a microscopic equivalent for Gay-Lussac's law.[8] Thus the observer would find physical realities beyond his sense of touch or sight, on a level above his own. But these realities would exist for him only when and where the molecules were numerous enough, and therefore dense enough, for him to observe large numbers of them. Otherwise, his results would merely be erratic.[9]

---

[8] Where volume is constant,
$$p = p_0 (1 + \alpha\, t),$$
where p is the pressure, t the temperature and α the coefficient of expansion of the gas observed.

[9] See the introduction to my *Théorie des phénomènes monétaires* (1927), and "L'Economie politique, sciences statistiques," in *Revue de Métaphysique et de Morale*, October-December 1925.

On the other hand, in those fields where the observer's size is of the same magnitude as that of the particles being observed —i.e. the human sciences, essentially—the separate elements, the "individuals," can be apprehended directly. At the same time, the global phenomenon remains beyond man's grasp, because he is too small to perceive it directly. In an environment of that type, man is in precisely the same situation as an intelligent bacterium seeking to work out the laws of gases. To determine such global entities (which are known nowadays as macroscopic realities or aggregates) as price levels, trade flows, employment levels, volume of consumption, investment, balance of payments, exchange rates, and the like, he can only rely on statistical methods to measure individual magnitudes and then make use of the averages. All this demonstrates how relative our notion of "substance" is. Particles or components must be of a certain smallness and density before they can become the constituents of some matter endowed with an existence of its own—like the water I plunge my hand into without being able to distinguish the molecules it is made of.

Even our thinking, because of language and writing, is subject to a certain fundamental quantification, in the form of words and notes. Each word or note in itself is a "particle" of thought or harmony. But when closely woven into a text, they melt into the continuum of a poem or a symphony. Thus the stuff of our universe is never homogeneous or isotropic, even when our senses tell us it is. It is consistently made up of particles, more or less independent of one another. These particles are the "quanta" of substance and allow us to say that, in our universe, every reality is "quantified."[10]

---

[10] This statement must nevertheless be qualified by recalling that there are some scores of fundamental particles at present known to scientists which have not yet been shown conclusively to be made of variously arranged particles of energy. This is not, however, an unlikely conclusion. All doubts will be dispelled when the nature of fundamental particles has been made clear.

The structure between the two poles of nothingness

All members of our universe "are of the dust and all turn to dust again." If we accept this statement by Ecclesiastes (III:20), then existence is only a time span—short or long—between two infinities of dust. Creation does not imply, therefore, any change of substance. It is basically a process which transforms scattered particles into an orderly whole. But this finding does not tell us anything at all about the nature of that transformation.

Actually, it is from our feeling that we exist throughout the time span separating our birth from our death that, by means of a process of generalization, we evolve the very notion of existence. We project it into the world around us and say that certain things, substantial or unsubstantial, "exist." Others —the dog's head we discern in a cloudy sky, for example— may occasionally become real but are not thereby necessarily endowed with existence.

It is for this reason that the atom exists for us and outside our own beings. The fundamental particles of which it is composed do not hurl themselves at one another to neutralize each other. Rather, even though they carry contrary electrical charges, they remain distinct within the shifting but stationary structure that encloses and unites them. The tiny universe of the atom is protected against all continuous change by the quantified nature of its components and by the equally quantified discontinuity of its possible states. There is no intermediate stage between it and the outer world. An electron may be inside or outside an atom, but if it moves from outside to inside, it will change the atom without cutting off its existence. Thus arises one of the major distinctive features of existence: identity through change over time.

There is no doubt that the molecules that unite atoms into durable structures also exist. In fact, the arrangement of their constituent atoms is one of their essential characteristics.

14

Nothing is more convincing in this respect than those large molecules—like DNA—whose structures can be drawn. They derive their characteristic properties from those structures. The molecule of nucleic acid even has the extraordinary capability of imposing its own structure on the group of molecules necessary for its reproduction; thus it is capable of generating existence. Similarly, a crystal is a form that endures, and Weisäcker considers its spatial symmetry to be its true reality.

The characteristics of existence are perceived even more clearly in animate beings. They come closer to what the existence of the human person reveals in a direct way. Cells exist because, despite their characterizing metabolism, the constantly renewed ensembles they constitute maintain a durable structure which the many hazards they face does not destroy. This is also the organs of living bodies: a plant's leaf, an animal's heart or stomach exist because, by organizing cells into characteristic structures, they perform specific functions, notwithstanding changes occurring in their condition or in their medium. On the other hand, cancer frequently terminates existence because it is a pathological condition in which one part of the organized structure "forgets all about the rest . . . and carries on . . . as if there was nobody else. . . ."[11]

During their lifetime, living beings are the clearest examples of existence, which in this case declares itself at their birth and ceases at death. Between these two poles of nonexistence, they evolve and change, all the while remaining themselves and using subtle mechanisms to defend their continuity as living beings against the destructive forces that assail them. What they preserve in this process is nothing other than the very structure to which they owe their existence.

This is François Jacob's opinion:

What characterizes a living being is the organization of its structures. Even so simple an object as the cell of

[11] Aldous Huxley, *Island*, 1962, p. 240.

a bacterium presents a degree of complexity difficult to conceive of . . . a cell cannot possibly be a mere collection of various molecules gathered into a bundle and subject to the laws of statistics which govern units arranged simply side by side and totally independent from one another. . . . There is no doubt that the properties of an organism amount to something more than the sum total of the properties of its constituents. Nature does more than merely add us: she integrates. Thus the power of reproducing a characteristic order belongs to a cell, and not to its constituent parts.[12]

At levels above individuals, many groups unquestionably present the characteristics of existence. Beehives and anthills exist as enduring structures despite the changes they undergo. Man also generates, in the form of superstructures, a series of organized groups which, one must acknowledge, present the characteristics of existence. The couple and the family, institutions which bind together individual behaviors, exist over extended time spans. A workshop, a farm, a business, and in the Army, a company, a battery, a battalion, or a division—all these are also organized ensembles endowed with existence. Each performs a characteristic service and is even consciously organized with a view to the production of that service; they remain in operation in adverse conditions and often assert themselves by fighting. All these features are signs of a specific existence which is more than the simple sum total of the separate existences of the constituent units.

The same may be said of a city, which brings together workers, businessmen, civil servants, and business firms in specific proportions. These are strictly in line with the functions the city is called upon to perform. Similarly, patriots have a heartfelt conviction of the existence of their nation. That existence is demonstrated by the fact that a nation may

[12] Inaugural lecture.

come into being and later die. History is the outcome of the efforts made by nations to defend their existence against threatening forces.

But existence is not the privilege of matter alone. A poem exists; it consists of the arrangement of its constituent words. However, it does not exist if those words are presented in a different order from that imposed on them by the poet. Though words existed before the act of poetic creation, the poem did not. On the other hand, a given arrangement need not be immutable to generate existence. All that is required is that it be stationary, or quasi-stationary—like the solar system, whose planets move indefinitely within their own orbits. Nor need the existent always be of the same matter. Constantly renewed ensembles—a country's population, for example, or the flame of a gas-burner—also exist.

The clearest example of an endlessly renewed existence is that of living beings. They evolve and change even while they maintain their identity. Their metabolism is the instrument of a process of assimilation which, despite constant changes of substance, ensures their fundamental unity and individuality.

The characteristics of existence are confirmed *a contrario* by the nature of those ensembles which seem to have no existence of their own. This is particularly true of the dust of cemeteries, the remains of what had been living bodies, or of the ruins of destroyed or deserted cities. They are what is left of disrupted structures. The whole of which they were once part has ceased to exist, though its components are still present.

The molecules of a gas are also in a state of nonexistence when the density of the gas is so weak that interactions among its elementary components cease for all practical purposes. Thus,

Stellar matter would seem to be a quasi-nuclear gas composed of very small atomic nuclei deprived of most of their electrons by high temperature and radiation. . . . Nearly all the matter of the Universe exists in this simple, nonorganized form. . . . Only the tiniest quantity, what constitutes stellar atmospheres, interstellar matter, and the planets, exists in the complex (highly structured) form familiar to us.[13]

The mark of states of nonexistence is not, as is too often claimed, that the characteristic factors of the constituents are distributed at random. Rather, each element is pursuing its own destiny, independently of the destinies of all the others. In other words, there is no interaction between them.

Thus a collectivity of bees constitutes a society, which is called a colony, and is endowed with all the characteristics of existence; a gang of cats, on the other hand, has no existence of its own—except when one or more of the females is in heat. Similarly, molecules or atoms grouped in a crystalline system constitute a genuine society, while those of a gas at high temperature remain independent of one another for long periods of time (except during those occasional clashes which bring them together temporarily). Their disorder, which has been designated Brownian motion, obviously shows no sign of an existence of its own.

> Existence always manifests itself as the result of a lasting arrangement, the establishment, therefore, of a certain "order" among elementary particles. The system of abstract relations common to all constituent elements of an "existent" defines its "structure." This last, an expression of the architecture governing its construction, can be considered the essence of its being.[14]

The elements of a structure derive their properties not only from their own nature, but also from their place and role

---

[13] A. Dauvilliers, *Cosmologie et chimie*, 1965, p. 7.
[14] Pierre Auguer, "L'Incarnation de la forme," *Revue Philosophique*, 1960.

in the "whole" of which they are members. Thus the whole is immensely different from the sum of its parts. The organic units derived from such structuring are individualized and limited in space or time. They are thus evident as "forms."[15] However, while substance and form can be considered independently of one another, they are indissolubly united within the "existent" which, for its part, is essentially the embodiment of a form.

Every existent endowed with a form is necessarily limited within space or time (subject to the interaction effects specified in the next chapter). Genuine discontinuities, therefore, separate it from all analogous existents. A particle "belongs" or "does not belong." Although it can—and in fact in general does—belong to several existents, it can only belong to each of them in part.

That which separates an existent's "within" from the infinity of its "without" is one of the principal characteristics of existence. Atomic physicists call this a "potential barrier." They study the quantitative characteristics of the "potential well" which encloses neutrons and protons and confers the privilege of existence upon the nucleus by protecting it from aggressive forces. According to this concept, the structure which generates existence is invested entirely in the lasting, immutable, or stationary arrangement of the elements which are its substance.

The next chapter will demonstrate that a structure is always the product of the interactions that link particles of existence. These interactions vary according to the nature of the order they generate. Our anthropomorphic interpretation of the universe always invests them with the characteristics of forces of attraction, since these are the foundation of our theoretical explanations of the physical world. Depending upon the level at which they operate, they may be given various labels:

[15] Sce Paul Guillaume, *Psychologie de la forme*.

exchange forces within the nucleus; electric or electromagnetic forces within the atom or the molecule; tropisms, appetencies, or appetites in an animal being; the will in a thinking being. In every case, regardless of the level at which they operate and notwithstanding our ignorance of their real nature and basic cause, they may genuinely be considered the coalescing agents of existence. All of them characteristically belong to the structures they organize, apart from any actions they may be capable of outside the particular structure's spatial or temporal limits. The interactions forming the atom, the molecule, the one- or multicellular living being, the family, or the city have no other source than their constituent elements. "Every organism is a self-singing melody."[16]

Elements of structures that decay are usually caught up into larger and less intense structures. Only rarely does it happen that a particle is subject to no interaction. In our world, terrestrial gravity plays an important role in collecting all heavy particles that are free. It is for this reason that the earth seems the cemetery of departed structures. Once they have escaped from the more powerful interactions that generated the structures to which they formerly belonged, the remains of living beings, the dust of ruins, and the sediment produced by the erosion of mountains join with the genuine nucleus our earthly globe constitutes to form less complex sedimentary structures.

In fact, any ensemble which appears structureless is usually a collection of particles subject to negligible interactions, at least so long as those particles are not close to certain similar or different particles with which they would interact. A photon in cosmic space, a stray cat not in heat, an anchorite in the desert, are all examples of particles of existence free from any social structure—except, of course, that the last two have

---

[16] Merleau-Ponty attributes this sentence to Nexhull and is reported to have found it, without any reference, in one of Buytendik's books: *La Structure du comportement*, 1933, p. 172.

a relationship to the earth forced upon them by terrestrial gravity.

The hierarchy of the various levels of organization

The foregoing analysis leads one to view every "existence" as the product of an arrangement of particles into a lasting, immutable, or stationary structure—that is, in effect, a "society." Thus an animal is a society of organs, each organ a society of cells, and each cell a society comprising a nucleus, a container, and the organized elements—organellae, or mitochondria—that make up protoplasm. Each of these organized elements is itself a society of protein chains, complicated arrangements of molecules of amino acids. In their turn, the amino acids are structured societies made of atoms of carbon, hydrogen, oxygen, and nitrogen. All of these elements are strung out in multiple spirals in which the location of each constituent plays a critical role. The atom is a society of protons, neutrons, and electrons, which are further organized groupings of dozens of fundamental particles whose existence is now an established fact. Contemporary science does not allow us to posit that these fundamental particles are the result of an arrangement of particles of energy or light, but recent advances in quantum physics tend to confirm that hypothesis.

Thus, with this single reservation, every existent can be broken down into a series of existents of an inferior order. Each existent is a society for the individuals preceding it and an individual for the society following it. On each level we encounter the two chasms where Pascal, in his anguish, saw "nothingness face to face with an infinite, a whole face to face with nothingness, a middle way between nothing and everything."

According to this analysis, all societies of a similar nature constitute a "level of organization." Thus we distinguish the particulate level, the nuclear level, the atomic level, the molecular level, the crystalline level, the viral level, the level of those organisms within a living cell (organellae, mitochondria), the cellular level, the organic level, the level of living beings. But, over and above living beings, we can see societies made up of couples or families—not only numerous types of animal societies, such as those of insects or of birds, but, as we reach man, the complex hierarchy of human societies: families, tribes, businesses, cities, nations, and, in recent times, communities or societies of nations.

I am aware that classifying human societies with animal or molecular societies will surprise and even shock some readers. I hope, however, that they will suspend judgement for a time. The remainder of this book will show that if these various societies have in common a feature that can properly be termed a social structure, that structure results, for each of them, from specific processes of association. Such processes confer on each of them its own originality and determine those characteristics customarily identified in each.

As a matter of fact, Father Teilhard de Chardin has already stressed the general and widespread nature of social structures and pointed out the pitfalls open to anyone overlooking them.

> Without any precise scientific reason, but simply as a result of impression and habit, we have become accustomed to separate from one another, as though they belonged to two different worlds, arrangements of individuals and arrangements of cells, considering only the latter as organic and natural, as opposed to the former, which have been relegated to the world of the mind and the artificial.[17]

Is there any need to stress how an understanding of the general and widespread nature of hierarchical structures of order clarifies the problem of "intermediate communities" discussed in politics?

[17] Pierre Teilhard de Chardin, *The Appearance of Man*, 1965.

Social hierarchical structures sometimes branch off into other types of organization: planets, stars, galaxies, societies of galaxies. . . . In every instance, though they may begin with fundamental particles—or even, as we said earlier, with particles of energy or light—such hierarchical structures culminate in states which are asocial or barely social. The individuals generated by the last integration affected by the hierarchical structure are free of all interaction, or so far apart from one another that any existing interaction can only have a negligible influence. Photons in the cosmos are, in varying degrees, examples of this, as are ions in certain solutions, electrons in metals which are good conductors, the molecules in a gas of weak density, amoebas and other unicellular beings in certain liquids, flies in the air, cats—except when in heat or when lactating—and nations, when they have not established any covenant or league between themselves.

The hierarchy of the levels of organization reveals the existence of increasing complexities and leads to the concept of "order quality." The quality of a given order is commensurate with the level at which it occurs in the hierarchical structure to which it belongs.

But the greatest merit of the knowledge of hierarchical structures of order is that it demonstrates that no order can exist unless it is derived from the order immediately below. As a result, creation is necessarily the outcome of a progressive evolution in the direction of increasing complexity. It is because of the inescapable nature of hierarchical structures of order that evolution is the supreme law of the universe.

CHAPTER II

The Individual and Society

The individual as a quantum of existence

INDIVIDUALITY IS AN anthropomorphic concept. It is the outcome of our projecting into the external world a notion which is familiar because, as a result of consciousness, we have full and immediate knowledge of it.

In a curious reversal, however, the study of individualities not immediately perceptible, like the atom—and especially Louis de Broglie's discovery of "wave-corpuscle" complementarity—has made possible a general theory of the individual. Such research casts further light on characteristics and operation of that particular category of individuals constituted of human persons.

The concept of individual is the essential key to explanation in many different areas because the world surrounding us is full of "things" whose reality consists, not of the substance composing them, but of a mysterious quality which establishes their unity and generates their "existence." Considered separately, an electron and proton do not make up an atom of hydrogen. For that to happen, there must be established between them those relationships that will generate a durable structure separated from everything else in the world, thus making it an "individual." The unity established in this way is the characteristic of "existence," and the "whole" of its reality is confirmed, *a contrario*, by the fact that it vanishes as soon as the bonds linking the electron and proton are broken. Restored to their initial liberty, they continue to exist, and with them the entire substance of the atom they had formed. However, the atom itself has unquestionably ceased to exist. Although it remains a possible form which favorable circumstances may yet restore to reality, it will not materialize until that time. In the same way, an automobile consists of many parts but does not exist until all of them have been assembled into a structure designed by its manufacturer to "create" a vehicle.

The same thing may be said of everything which "exists" in our universe. Specifically, the individual constituted as a living being is made up of innumerable elements but cannot be said to exist until all of these elements have been assembled into a structure that will engender life. In the same way, the unity of a married couple is certainly endowed with existence. The number of elements that compose the relationship is always a multiple of one, and therefore never fractional; but they will never constitute a "marriage" until and unless the bonds uniting male and female have been established, *de jure* or *de facto*. And that relationship will no longer exist if divorce or separation destroys the conjugal bond that created it.

Thus individuality is not indivisible, as the primal atom seemed to be. However, what is indivisible is its very existence, for if the individual is broken down, he ceases to exist. Therefore, individuality appears on the various levels of social stratification as a genuine "quantum" of existence.

Because it is so widespread and assumes such a diverse range of forms, the concept of the individual is not amenable to precise definition. But its dominant characteristic, as also its greatest mystery, is the unity which is its very substance.

We are individuals because everything that makes us what we are is ours. Our past and our possible future refer to undefinable but nevertheless real entity which is precisely the person whose medium we are. It is this unity of reference which weaves into one single history all the constituents of individuality, no matter how widely scattered over time or space they may be. Similarly, the electrons, protons, and neutrons making up an atom are separate and may have come into being at different times; but so long as the atom exists they belong to it, like the members of one family.[1]

Thus, the individual is an entity, a whole distinct from the rest of the universe and endowed with a certain freedom in relation to it. Its essential characteristic is that, so long as it exists, it can be affected by outside influences, even by changes in its constituent elements, while preserving its identity. Accidents, may impinge on it, of course, but unless they kill it, they will, through some kind of basic metabolism, become part of its own substance.

Because of this characteristic unity, everything that happens to an individual is part of it. Thus Zarathustra—that archetype of the individual—says, "the time has gone when I could expect chance events. What is it that can happen to me now that does not already belong to me?"

This ability to assimilate external events makes every individual the medium of a history which unlocks its destiny and renders it nameable. Within the uncoordinated unfolding of instantaneous events, individuality thus appears as some-

---

[1] After reading my manuscript, Pierre Auger sent me the text of a curious lecture delivered in English at the beginning of 1859 by Rudolf Virchoff, Professor of Pathology at Berlin and the champion of the medical application of the cellular theory. Anticipating the discovery of modern physics, Virchoff stressed the similarity between atoms and the individuals: "Both words have exactly the same meaning, though they connote different things. . . . The Latin word *individuus* means *atomos*, in Greek, and Aristotle himself ascribes to the latter the meaning of the former. They both mean the indivisible, the totality, the unity.

thing permanent. Whether of short or long (but always positive) duration, this permanence, as soon as it is illuminated by consciousness, gives rise to the fundamental concept of the human person.

The individual, a medium of behavior

If we agree with Merleau-Ponty that "behavior is a certain way of dealing with the world, of existing,"[2] then every being has a behavior. There is no question that human beings have a specific behavior. We know that each of our fellow beings always remains himself, except during lapses brought on by grave circumstances or of profound disturbances. We base all our judgements of men on this consistency in their modes of existence.

What may be said of men, however, is no less true of every living being and of every individual element comprising it. Dogs, bees, the stomach or the heart, spermatazoa, leucocytes, and amoebas **all** have a characteristic behavior. A recent television documentary showed the devouring attack of living amoebas on a dead cell just killed by an ultraviolet ray. The effort to reach their prey made by some amoebas which had arrived later than their fellows left no doubt—all anthropomorphism aside—that they behave in a characteristic way. Similarly, a spermatazoon on its way to an ovum exhibits a permanence of action, if not of intention, which betokens consistency of behavior. On a fluoroscope of the human stomach one can observe the regularly spaced contractions that bring about digestion of a fatty substance. This behavior is so constant that it is, to some extent at least, possible to diagnose a pathological condition from the slightest variation in the interval between contractions. A tree thrusting its roots down into the nourishing mould or its branches up toward

[2] Merleau-Ponty, *La Structure du comportement*, p. 136.

the light and the convolvulus pointing toward the stem around which it will wind itself also give evidence of dealing with the world around them in a characteristic way.

But what is true of living beings is even more so of inanimate things. Iron in the presence of sulphuric acid, silver nitrate exposed to sunlight, and an electron facing a proton, all behave in a perfectly fixed way. So also do fundamental particles, which are specifically characterized by the duration of their existence.

It goes without saying that if the way in which beings conduct themselves were erratic, it would be impossible, at least without begging the question, to speak of behavior and to consider it characteristic of the beings exhibiting it. In fact, the individual is "an enduring identity" only because it reacts to surrounding circumstances in a way which virtually never changes. Its behavior is the direct expression and the immediate consequence of its existence. As Raymond Ruyer puts it, "physical individualities exist only in so far as they exhibit behavior." Their behavior is the temporal aspect of their existence, as structure is the spatial aspect of some of them.

Behavior, contrary to macroscopic phenomena, always involves a certain margin of indeterminacy

Though behavior is characteristic of existence, whose temporal expression it is, it is never strictly determined.

As already pointed out, human beings always remain nearly identical with themselves. Nevertheless, their behavior can never be predicted with certainty. It will always fall within the range of their physical and psychic possibilities, of course, but, given the realm of potentialities thus defined, actual behavior never attains more than a certain degree of probability. Thus it constitutes a random event.

Nothing is more characteristic in this regard than the duration of human life, because it corresponds to the type of behavior that is most clearly defined and easiest to study. At each stage in his existence, an individual, considered separately, has a certain life expectancy. This in no way enables him to foresee the date of his death, but it does confer upon each possible date a well-defined degree of probability.

Other aspects of human behavior—health, love, hate, good or evil actions—may be more difficult to explore, but they nevertheless exhibit the same character: they are unpredictable "ways of being," and only their degree of probability can be assessed. Viewed from outside, as exhibited by other people, they appear as spontaneous outbursts, characteristic appearances of the individual who is at one and the same time their subject and their object.

These are the marks which differentiate the behavior of a particular individual from any collective phenomenon brought about by a large number of separate individual actions. The latter, as such, can be predicted with accuracy and, other things being equal, obeys strict laws. Thus the timing of the deaths of a million babies considered at the time of their births —a macroscopic phenomenon which stands in opposition to the microscopic phenomenon of an individual death—is fully predictable; its degree of fixity is evidenced in the profits of life insurance companies.

The study of suicide leads to similar conclusions. For any individual considered separately, the unpredictability of the event is virtually absolute; only its degree of probability can be established. But as regards large populations, the stability of percentage and the resulting possibilities of prediction have led certain authors to speak of a veritable conscription of suicides.

If we watch a dog or a cat, it is clear that at every moment its behavior is unpredictable. Nevertheless, we know that, in certain circumstances, any of its possible actions has a degree of probability that can be assessed. Similarly, an amoeba that is close to a possible prey and a spermatazoon that is not far from an ovum will follow paths which cannot be marked out beforehand, and which are therefore unequally probable; but they become certain for a larger population of individuals.

Formerly, it was held that indeterminism pertained only to vital phenomena. Inanimate nature, in its passivity, was considered the realm of strict determination. But the discovery of radioactive decay should have prompted further reflection. In 1896 Henri Becquerel established that a heavy element, uranium, spontaneously emitted certain rays. Pierre and Marie Curie extended this discovery to thorium, then to polonium and radium. Finally, in 1934, the Joliot-Curies demonstrated that nuclear transmutations could yield other so-called artificial radioactive elements, distributed over the entire Periodic Table.

Note that all these radioactive elements obey virtually the same law of decomposition. We cannot predict when any particular atom will decompose. All we can do is attribute to it a certain "life expectancy," positing the probability of its decomposition at any particular moment. On the other hand, when dealing with a great number of atoms, it is possible to predict the rate at which the process of decomposition will occur over time; the greater the number of atoms, the more accurate the confirmation of the prediction by the event.

It was not until Werner Heisenberg formulated his uncertainty principle, that it was apparent how widespread the indeterminism of individual behavior is. Indeed, quantum mechanics has discarded the idea that the location of a particle in space can be predicted. It claims only that the particle will necessarily be in the region occupied by its wave, and that the greater the amplitude of the wave at one particular point, the stronger the chance that the particle is there. Whereas traditional physics claimed to bring all physical phenomena under rigorous and inexorable laws, modern physics provides nothing but estimates of probability. These leave a margin of uncertainty in the expression of phenomena.

Niels Bohr, emphasizing that uncertainty, concluded that quantum physics weakened or made more uncertain the distinction between the objective and the subjective. Louis de Broglie goes farther and wonders whether

> the new ideas of contemporary physics will not allow us to understand why the conventional methods of objective science seem to adapt themselves with difficulty to the phenomena of the vital order and the mental order, so that . . . microscopic physics would function as an intermediary between macroscopic physical reality, where mechanism and determinism are valid, and other, more subtle, spheres in which the same notions would be, if not wrong, at least unusable.[3]

In a book published in 1934, the question was carried to a higher level still by the famous mathematician John von Neumann, who raised the whole problem of causality:

> There is nothing in macroscopic physics which proves causality, because the apparent causal order of the macroscopic world has no other origin than the law of large numbers, and independently of the fact that elementary processes (the genuine physical processes) do or do not obey causal laws. . . . It is only on the level of the atom, in the very elementary processes themselves, that the question of causality can really be put to the test; but on this level with the present state of our knowledge, everything points away from it, since the only formal theory which nearly coincides with experience and summarizes it is quantum mechanics, which is at completely logical odds with causality. . . . There is no longer any reason today which permits us to affirm the existence of causality in Nature; no experiment could prove it, because macroscopic phenomena, by their very nature,

[3] *Matter and Light*, p. 261.

are incapable of furnishing such proof, and the only theory compatible with our knowledge of elementary phenomena leads one to reject it.

Citing this passage, Louis de Broglie observes that "for Neumann and for most of today's quantum physicists, the determinism of macroscopic phenomena is an illusion due to the play of averages, a simple statistical appearance." He adds that, with science in its present state, "it is impossible to reduce, by the introduction of hidden variables, quantum indeterminism to underlying determinism." He concludes by emphasizing that the interest in these considerations "is not limited to the physical sciences, but extends to the human sciences as well, sciences whose laws, because the phenomena they examine are always very complex, are necessarily of a statistical nature."[4]

One would be in danger of misinterpreting Broglie, however, if one did not qualify these observations by mentioning his own reservation, which he expressed in a footnote. He says that although indeterminacy breaks any rigorous chain of causality, "it nevertheless does not imply that all possibilities are equally probable. Every 'state' of a microscopic system acknowledges certain 'tendencies' which express themselves through the differing probabilities of the various possibilities the system harbors." So precisely does this remark apply to human phenomena that it provides a link between the physical and the human sciences.

Actually, conventional views led to a clear-cut opposition

[4] Louis de Broglie, *Physics and Microphysics*, 1955, pp. 201–202. In *Certitudes et incertitudes de la science* (1966), however, Broglie explains the scruples, and even doubts, which, in the latest state of his thinking, led him to this conclusion. In a letter to the author, dated December 24, 1966, he pointed out that the lines in question were written at a time when he was a proponent of the ideas of the Copenhagen school, which he then supported, but that he had since returned to the notions which guided him after the discovery of wave-mechanics and had adopted a very different way of looking at things. For further details, see the Postscript to this chapter.

between "proper" scientific predictability and the predictability of human behavior. The former was declared to be absolute and rigorous, the latter contingent and nearly always doubtful.

Though we can make advance calculations about the movements of the planets in great detail without the slightest suggestion of uncertainty, when it comes to the reactions of a man, we limit ourselves to predictions in broadest outline; we usually have to leave the door open to several possibilities, one or another of which we calculate will win the day.[5]

But the contradiction disappears in the light of quantum physics:

It shows us that the difference established in the light of our examples is not really a difference between physics and biology, but between macrophysics and biology. Only in physics dealing with bodies of extremely large dimensions—extremely large compared to the dimensions of atoms and molecules—is it possible, as in the case of planetary motion for instance, to make strict predictions without leaving some leeway as to the phenomena to be expected. The tiniest particles—atoms, electrons, photons—on the other hand, are subject to physical laws which forbid univocal and precise prediction. . . . It is no more possible to make strict predictions about microphysical events than it is in biology. If it is possible in macrophysics—even though every macrophysical body is composed of atoms and, therefore, every macrophysical event is made up of elementary microphysical events which are not discretely foreseeable—this is because very precise statistical laws are nonetheless valid for atomic reactions; each possibility for reaction is affected by a

---

[5] Pascual Jordan, *La Physique et la secret de la vie organique*, 1959, pp. 207–208. (German version published in 1948.)

strictly determined coefficient of probability. Consequently, the concern of macrophysics, i.e. the average behavior of a large number of atoms of the same sort, is susceptible to rigorous prediction, despite the unpredictability of individual reactions: just as the average behavior of a herd of cattle or of the population of a large city is predictable, despite the unpredictability of some of the individuals involved. . . . The equivocal nature of microphysical predictions, therefore, is not the result of faulty or incomplete knowledge; it is the unavoidable effect of the nature of things. It is an ineluctable law of macroscopic physics that similar conditions give rise to similar consequences; in microphysics, the situation is, quite simply, different.[6]

The difference between the microscopic and macroscopic orders lies essentially in the fact that the former is the result of the behavior of individuals, the latter, of aggregates that are subject to the law of large numbers:

We are aware that recent efforts tending toward an elaboration of specifically biological notions and laws have stressed individuality as a biological phenomenon; every enterprise labeled "totality" begins with the fact that substances endowed with life present themselves to us only in the form of delimited individuals. There is no analogous phenomenon in the macrophysical order. On the other hand, the moment one moves into microphysics, one finds individuals whose nature is not biological but which are quite clearly defined. We see, in fact, that matter and radiation are entirely composed of numerous individuals, such as atoms, photons, electrons. . . . And certain recent experimental discoveries demonstrate that the apparent resemblance between biology and microphysics is neither

[6] Ibid., pp. 209–212.

34

fortuitous nor insignificant. The research into viruses which has proved that they are crystallizable has bridged the gulf that seemed to exist between the largest individuals in molecular physics and the smallest ones in biology: the viral individuals—formations which, despite their simplicity, nevertheless present properties characteristic of living beings—are nothing other than very large molecules. Beginning with electrons and atomic nuclei and passing through atoms and molecules, we arrive, through increasing complexity, at the individuals of the organic world: this is a striking indication that the laws of quantum physics, which govern individuals of an inferior order, unavoidably continue to exercise a decisive influence upon individuals of a higher order.[7]

Because it is an organized whole, a "totality" not subject to the law of large numbers, the individual is everywhere a medium of indeterminacy.

Heisenberg's uncertainty principle reduces universal determinism, which is the product of the law of large numbers, to a purely global appearance. It undermines Laplace's famous dictum in his Essay on the Calculus of Probabilities:

an intelligence which, at any given moment, could know all the forces animating Nature and the respective positions of all the beings of which it is composed, provided of course it was of an all-embracing nature so as to analyze all these data, would in a single formula encompass the motions of the largest bodies in the universe and those of the tiniest atom; nothing would be uncertain to it, and the future as well as the past would be before its eyes.[8]

---

[7] Ibid., pp. 218–219.
[8] *Théorie analytique des probabilités*, 3rd ed., 1820, "Introduction," p. 20.

It was obvious that if the behavior of the particle was determined, the whole world itself had to be determined as well. But the slightest symphony or the most obscure poem was enough to demonstrate the invalidity of such a statement. If it was to be consciously rejected, however, indeterminacy had to be brought into our universe. And it was the individual that opened the way along which, with the progress of living species, the long procession of liberty would travel.

There is something piquant in the fact that the purely mathematical discovery of the uncertainty principle by Heisenberg was necessary before we could recognize that there is fundamental indeterminacy in the world. All the time our experience of our creative liberty afforded us an unquestionable and immediate knowledge of that fact. Contrary to a widespread opinion, the advance of quantum mechanics has brought us to a view of the universe that no longer offends common sense as Laplace's statement did.

Individual psychism, the determinant of the indeterminate

What is characteristic of behavior and distinguishes it from a physical phenomenon is its random nature. All we know is that each of the events of which it is the global expression will occur within an area of uncertainty—not necessarily spatial—where the probability of its occurring is not zero. Each constituent element within this area can be assigned a coefficient defining the probability that the event will be localized there.

Because of this random nature, behavior, an individual phenomenon, is profoundly different from macroscopic phenomena, which are the products of the law of large numbers. The randomness of an event is difficult to ascertain experimentally: although it is relatively easy to ascertain what actually is, one cannot observe what is not but might have been. We acquire direct awareness of randomness only with regard to those events we ourselves bring about. As we do so, we are aware that they are the results of more or less voluntary choices from many possibilities. The more deliberate the choices, the freer they seem. But in every instance they appear to be endowed with a certain kind of creative spontaneousness. Hence they are, so to speak, ever-renewed inventions.

However, this selection process is perceived only in respect to those acts that we effect consciously. And these constitute only a small part of the range of events in the human organism. We have no more information about how unconscious acts are effected than we do about the sources of animal behavior. Nevertheless, both types—the reflex behaviors of my body and the behavior of a bird flying about in my garden—seem to the outside observer to evade all possibility of rigorous predictability. They evince a kind of apparent spontaneity which, although on a different scale, is reminiscent of the spontaneity of conscious acts.

Microscopic or ultra-microscopic observation of an amoeba's behavior in relation to a possible prey, or of a population of spermatozoa in the presence of an ovum, forces us to construe such events as individual behaviors, rather than determined physical phenomena. Similarly, although radioactive disintegration is strictly determined for a mass composed of a great number of atoms, it remains entirely unpredictable in terms of an isolated atom. Each such atom is radioactive only once in its lifetime—but we never know when it will be. All we can do is assess the probability of its decay at a given moment. Thus we are fully justified in identifying the spontaneity of an atom's decomposition as the hallmark of a genuine behavioral phenomenon.

In the same way, ever since Heisenberg's discovery of the uncertainty principle we have known that no unequivocal predictions can be made concerning the location of particles in space. Pascual Jordan goes so far as to claim that the reactions of an isolated atom or molecule are not causally determined with certainty by any actions to which it may be subject. He argues that every molecule has a "choice" among a series of possible reactions and that each choice is made in accordance with constant laws of probability. Such an anthropomorphic interpretation strikes me as rather rash. One cannot reasonably infer, from the fact that behavior is a self-singing melody, that a pianist is at the piano. It is enough to recognize in the indeterminacy of individual paths the creative spontaneity that characterizes behavioral phenomena.

Individual behavior, however, preserves its random characteristic only to the extent that it has not yet come to pass. As soon as it becomes a thing of the past, it is entirely knowable, even if not entirely known. A refusal to admit the existence of effects without causes forces one to consider the determination of the indeterminate as the result of a process which selects, out of everything that could be, what actually will be. Generally speaking, we are unable to grasp the full nature of the selection process. We do, however, attain immediate cognition of it in the case of a conscious action, when we ourselves are the authors of the decision which will extract an accomplished act from the vast limbo of possible actions.

In fact, we perceive directly and immediately within ourselves the entire chain of causation of which our act is the outcome: I eat because I am hungry; I look after my children because I love them. The "I" here is the personal agent aware he is acting, or the thinking person who knows he is thinking. It cannot be located; the most that can be known is that it is somehow identified with the individual who is its medium. Generalizing the lessons that the various experiences of life teach us, we agree that certain circumstances give rise, in the person confronting them, to volitions that form a sort of impulse urging him toward the act they tend to trigger off.

Frequently, however, behavior is more impulsive than deliberate. Here the distinction between the volition and the act which follows it is artificial and fictitious. The former is the inner side, the latter the outer side, of one and the same reality—namely, behavior as it is actually observed. Only in certain extreme forms of conscious action is the distinction between volition and act as clearly marked as that between cause and effect. In such cases pursuit of a specific end, and therefore the desire to attain it, is the prime mover. The choice then is of the means conducive to attainment of that end. Operational calculus, with its rigor, provides a clear image of consciously finalized action. Action of that type is fully accounted for by the quest of the results it can yield.

In its own field, i.e. as regards acts of a typically economic nature, economic theory has systematized such choices. Each individual is allocated a scale of values and every item of wealth he is capable of acquiring is assigned its particular degree of satisfaction. As a result of this artificial device, *homo oeconomicus* becomes a seeker of maximum satisfaction and his behavior is explained in terms of that quest.

This is the sort of explanation we project beyond ourselves. Any behavior of whose cause we are unaware, because it is the behavior of someone other than ourselves, is declared to be the result of an analogous process of elaboration. We assume that the beings around us act deliberately: if a man courts a woman, it is because they are sexually attracted to one another. In the same way, we believe that voluntary action also explains the behavior of higher animals: if a cat suckles and licks her kittens, it is because (we think) she loves them; a bird gathering food into its nest is anxious to preserve its offspring. But experience proves that this is not at all the case: if one removes the bottom from the nest where the bird accumulates food, it will continue to pursue what has now become a vain activity.[9] Nevertheless, this sort of explanation is so deeply rooted that we apply it to every individual behavior:

[9] Konrad Lorenz, *King Solomon's Ring;* quoted by Dr. Paul Chauchard in *Des Animaux à l'homme*, p. 90.

a tree grows up through the surrounding branches of a forest because it is seeking the light it needs; a spermatozoon races toward an ovum because it is attracted to it, as male to female.

The same theory has been extended to explain the inanimate world, especially in the theory of motion. We know that a moving body does not change its motion unless we push or pull it with our arms. We represent forces in terms of similar interventions, and, where no human activity intervenes, we say that the changes are produced by the attractions or repulsions between the material bodies they affect. The notion of a field enables us to describe the complex of forces exerted within a given area of space.

Only in its most recent advances has quantum physics substituted impersonal and mathematical objectivity for such anthropomorphic explanations, which were clearly becoming inadequate. But in all those areas which remain liable to concrete representation, explanation of behaviors always correlates the behaving individual and the world surrounding it. Thus each individual is endowed with its own "nature," the product of its structure, which reacts in a determined and seemingly uniform manner to information derived from the outside world: man reacts to cold or hunger; the sex glands react to messages conveyed to them by certain hormones; the electron reacts to an electric or magnetic field. As Montaigne put it, "If I were pressed to say why I loved him, I feel that my only reply could be: because it was he; because it was I."[10] Through the "he" and the "I," behavior ceases to be a spontaneous outburst, impervious to human intelligence, and becomes the outcome of an unending exchange between the "nature" of the agent and the "nature" of the world surrounding him.

By means of this distinction between "the inside" and "the outside," we succeed in rationalizing individual behavior. It becomes the logical consequences of causes that explain it

[10] *Essais*, I, xxvii.

all the better because they were created—like those notions consciousness makes us aware of—precisely to explain it.

When it confirms our experience—i.e. when it is "true" in the scientific sense of the world—such representation provides the means to modify individual behavior. Later chapters of this book, those devoted to the world and acts of Prometheus, will show that man's operations on reality and the prodigious power that science has vested in him are exercised through modifications of the natures of individuals, or of the messages they receive from the world surrounding them.

I use the term "psychism" to designate the complex of faculties that determines an individual's behavior in response to the messages he receives from the outside world. These are mainly the messages that reach the sensory system. When they have been refined and interpreted, they generate volitions which will then be converted into acts.

A study of behavioral diseases shows conclusively that such processes are related to the integrity of the cerebral apparatus and its nervous connections. The more elaborate the neural equipment, the more complex and subtle the refining and interpreting processes. But it would be a serious mistake to consider the highest forms of psychism—i.e. conscious action or, more typically, reasoned action—a mere reflection of biological phenomena. For example, the discovery that a particular sensory excitation was the result of a change in the electric charge or the surface tension of a nerve cell would not make it any easier to understand the gestures it can produce. The definition of sound as vibration of air certainly makes acoustical physics possible, but it does not explain Beethoven's Fifth Symphony—any more than knowledge of sex hormones can explain love to a man who has never experienced it.[11] Furthermore, "the existence of conditioned reactions in fish which

[11] On this subject, see Buytendijk and Plesser, *Die psychologische Erklärung des Verhaltens*, p. 163.

do not have a cerebral cortex or even in invertebrates and down to protozoa suggests that these reactions are not linked to any particular anatomical device and that they must be the expressions of a general property of nervous phenomena or even of biological phenomena."[12]

We know nothing more about the nature of the process that orientates the speed of molecules in an electrical field—or, to put it more anthropomorphically, that causes them to follow parallel paths. The most familiar mystery concerns energy and the way it generates motion, is stored, or is transferred. Thus, very generally, in every example the behavior of elementary particles seems to be a spontaneous outburst, an "emergence" characteristic of the individual which is at one and the same time its subject and its object.

For human beings, behavior is distinct from existence because they categorize our observations according to time and space. We call an individual's spatial appearance its existence and its temporal activity its behavior. But behavior and existence are actually indivisibly associated. Together, they make up the entire "personality"—that is, the human interpretation, in terms of personal experience, of the "quantification" that characterizes all the structures of the human universe at its various levels of organization.

Society, a bundle of coordinated behavior

Despite its apparent unity, every individual, to anyone analyzing its internal structure, is a society made up of individuals of an immediately inferior rank. But as they combined into this society, all these individuals lost their innate independence, at least so far as certain aspects of their behavior are concerned.

An electron that has entered an atom will no longer be

---

[12] Merleau-Ponty, *La Structure du comportement*, p. 66.

a particle coursing about in infinite space at its own speed. Its location in space will be subject to certain probability requirements, which will, in fact, restrict it to specific areas of space. It has ceased to be the independent individual it was before it became a member of a society. Subject to its own margin of uncertainty, i.e. the amount of liberty left to it, it will have become an individual controlled by the requirement of the social order to which it now belongs. Similarly, atoms which have combined into a molecular or crystalline society are no longer that population of virtually independent particles constituting stellar matter, but a group of individuals controlled by the exigencies of that order of which they are parts. Again, the organs constituting a human body do not have an independent and autonomous life. Their behavior is controlled in a similar way by the exigencies of the "whole" to which they belong. If this "whole" goes up a stairway, its heart beats more quickly and the oxygen consumption of its cells increases.

The coordination of behavior that generates a social order becomes quite clear when human societies are considered. The partners in a marriage no longer enjoy autonomous behavior as they did single. Similarly, a factory worker, a soldier in the army, a musician in an orchestra, all behave in accordance with the requirements of the societies of which they are members, at least so far as those of their activities affecting the social order are concerned.

Thus, if a society is to exist, each of its constituent members must act in accordance with the requirements of the whole of which it is a part; in other words, all individual behaviors must submit to the requirements of the whole. It is this control over some aspects of individual behaviors that generates a social state: a population of individuals is transformed into a new individual of the next higher rank consisting of the society they form.

The concept of "control" is familiar to mechanical engineers,

43

especially to students of or experts in cybernetics. They ascribe very different meanings to the term. I shall retain in particular the one mentioned by Mr. Naslin in an article published in *Revue d'optique*. He finds the function of control systems to be the establishment of a specific relation between one or several magnitudes, the "input magnitudes," and one or several other magnitudes worked out by the system, the "output magnitudes." [13]

The notion of "control" is even more general. It seems to me to include any processes that deflect, inflect, or modify individual behavior by subjecting it to disciplines that generate a social order. In terms of this definition—and I realize that it is a large-scale generalization of the kind cyberneticists rely upon—societies are always the outcome of individual behavior that is subjected to the requirements of the social order.

Interaction, the mainspring of all existence

Considering the numerous societies that make up our universe, it is clear that, notwithstanding their enduring nature, they are not brought about or maintained with the help of chains or supports of any kind. Paul Valéry stressed this fact and reached the conclusion that there is no "power capable of creating order by mere physical coercion." [14] And yet the atom, the molecule, the living being, the family, the firm, the city, the state, each enclose individuals in various types of enduring social orders. Such orders are the mainspring of all existence.

If one is not prepared to believe that there can be effects without causes, then the coordination of individual behavior without which no society could possibly exist must indicate that the behavior of the individuals whose coexistence generates

[13] *Les Systèmes asservis*, in *Revue d'optique*, 1951. See also, and above all, Albert Ducrocq, *La Logique de la vie*. pp. 36 ff.
[14] Preface to *Lettres persones*.

a society is affected by external influences. These must originate either from fellow members of the society or from a dominant individual. In each and every case, the coordinating action is remote; that is, it is an "interaction" influencing the behavior of the individual subjected to it.

Is it possible, for example, to imagine the existence of an atom without some remote action between the electron and the proton, or the existence of the interdependent whole that the living being represents without some coordinating action—i.e. interaction—between its constituent organs? Similarly, is it not through an action from a distance, i.e. an interaction, that the ovum attracts the spermatozoon, that sexual behavior is determined, that motherly love is awakened in a cat nursing her kittens, that a soldier's action is ordered by his officer or a factory worker's by his foreman? In each and every case interaction unites the members of a social order into a society. And since every creative process implies the formation of a society, interaction thus seems to be the true mainspring of "existence."

Remote actions assume various forms in our universe. Initially, they were identified and studied under the rubric of forces in the field of mechanics, especially celestial mechanics. The notion of universal attraction, for which Newton was responsible, was later extended to include electric and magnetic attraction.

However, the widespread and crucial nature of interaction phenomenon was long concealed by the apparent antinomy in nature between the "wave" aspect and the "corpuscle" aspect. In the brilliant synthesis of the "wave mechanics" theory, Louis de Broglie demonstrated the relationships between the two. Thus it was possible to evolve a quantum philosophy of the universe that is applicable not only to the physical sciences but to all human sciences as well:

> In physics, as in every other branch of knowledge, the problem of continuity and discontinuity has always

existed. In that science, as elsewhere, the human mind has always evinced two tendencies which are both antagonistic and complementary: on the one hand, the tendency to reduce the complexity of phenomena to the existence of simple, indivisible, and enumerable elements, a tendency whose analysis of reality attempts to reduce it to a dust cloud of individuals; on the other hand, there is the tendency which derives from our intuitive notion of time and space, notes the universal interaction of things and considers artificial any attempt to carve, so to say, definite individual entities out of the continuing flow of natural phenomena. . . .

Pushed to the extreme and opposed to one another, the concepts of continuity and discontinuity are incapable of translating reality which requires a subtle and almost undefinable fusion of the two terms of this antinomy. . . .

Let us consider first the discontinuous. In physics, since the time of the ancient philosophers, the tendency toward the discontinuous has consistently found its expression in atomic or corpuscular theories. Their ultimate aim has been to reduce matter to nothing more than a conglomeration of indivisible elementary particles, to break it down into discrete individuals fully localized in space. . . .

But the weakness of such a concept, carried to an extreme, was immediately evident. Like Leibniz's monads, these isolated elementary particles, devoid of extension, could not react on each other from a distance because, *ex hypothesis*, there was nothing outside them, nothing in the space separating them; nor could they react by contact through impact, as we say in mechanics, because considering that they are pinpoint particles they could not come in contact with each other without coalescing. . . . To construct a physics with these elementary corpuscles, the champions of the discontinuous had to adulterate their doctrine. . . . They could not account for the fact that there was interaction among the particles and could not regard them as anything except isolated entities unless they admitted—as they did—that they were generators and centers of forces and could attract or repel each other from a distance. . . . This came down to saying that the presence of a corpuscle changed the properties of all the space surrounding it; in other words, the corpuscle was only the center of an extended phenomenon. Thus, by renouncing the notion of the discontinuous in all its purity, a kind of compromise was reached, under which matter appeared as consisting of individual entities with extension in space, but organized around a pinpoint center.[15]

This conclusion led de Broglie to the fundamental idea from which he evolved his "wave mechanics":

This fundamental idea is that it is essential to introduce simultaneously the notion of the corpuscle and of the wave into every branch of physics, into the theory of matter as well as the theory of light, with every corpuscle considered as accompanied by a certain wave and every wave linked to the motion of one or more corpuscles. There were sound reasons, under the erstwhile theory of mechanics, for accepting this view, from which one could deduce the relations which must exist between the magnitudes which characterize the corpuscle and those which define its associated wave. . . .

Just as in the case of the physical point of classical mechanics, surrounded by its field of force, the synthesis of the continuous and the discontinuous is effected through the intermediary of individuals which are extended but are organized around a center. Such a representation makes it possible to preserve in all their purity

[15] *Matter and Light*, pp. 217–220.

the notion of causality, together with the traditional way of representing phenomena within the framework of time and space.[16]

Unfortunately, subsequent progress in physics made it impossible to retain this concrete representation. One had to admit that

the corpuscle, in a sense, is "free" to manifest itself here or there, with varying energy values, but that, given initial data, we can calculate exactly the probability that it will make one choice rather than another. . . . The above ideas, however, raise a serious question: if they are correct, how does it happen that mechanical phenomena occurring on our own scale seem to be governed by strict determinism? This objection can be met, however. If we take the macroscopic phenomena which classical mechanics can correctly account for, and calculate numerically the essential indetermination introduced by the new ideas, we find that it is always much less than the accidental indetermination due to lack of accuracy in measurement. Under these conditions, essential indetermination is completely masked by errors in experiment, and everything happens as though it did not exist at all. In other words, each corpuscle, in each of its manifestations, has always, as it were, a certain choice to make among several possibilities; but the limits of this choice are so narrow that everything happens as though instead of a free choice there were strict determination. Thus the apparent determinism of large-scale phenomena does not conflict with the notions of the new mechanics. . . .

Let us now sum up the ideas we have developed to this point. On the microscopic scale, physical reality appears to be composed of units which undergo successive

[16] Ibid., pp. 225, 226.

transformations, marked by sudden transitions, and such transformations cannot be described in terms of infinitesimal analysis within the framework of continuity and determinism. But the statistical aspect of these kaleidoscopic transformations, for its part, can be described in conventional terms if we resort to the artifice of the associated waves concept. When we move up to the macroscopic world, the discontinuous nature of these individual phenomena disappears, drowned as it were in the statistical reality. The complementary and more or less irreconcilable descriptions in terms of wave and corpuscle, space-time localization, and dynamic state, combine and coalesce in the strict and harmonious mould of classical physics. . . .

Must we go still farther and believe, as Mr. Bohr seems to suggest, that the new concepts of contemporary physics will enable us to understand why the classical methods of objective science do not seem to adjust easily to vital and mental phenomena, so that . . . microscopic physics would function as an intermediary between macroscopic physical reality, where mechanism and determinism are valid, and other, more subtle, spheres in which the same notions would be, if not erroneous, at least unavailing? As a physicist, I shall not attempt an answer to this question. I shall, instead, limit myself to concluding that the discovery of quanta, the consequences of which are only now beginning to become evident in all their scope, seems to require of scientific thought one of the greatest changes in orientation it has ever had to make in its secular effort so that our idea of the physical world should, to the greatest extent possible, be amenable to the requirements of our reason.[17]

The effort de Broglie invites us to make is clearly less great

[17] Ibid., pp. 229, 230, 260–261.

than he imagines. There is a strange paradox in the discovery of wave-corpuscle complementarity in the atomic universe: the human sciences should long ago have brought it to our attention and made it the foundation of all our explanatory theories.

Can one fail to notice the obvious existence of remote actions when one considers human or animal societies? Anyone who has seen through a microscope a spermatozoon rush toward an ovum, or who has heard a stallion neighing after a mare or witnessed the mating dances that precede sexual intercourse among so many living species, cannot doubt the existence of effective interactions between the opposite sexes. Is it not remarkable that the basis for interaction found throughout nature is the binary principle? Energy is available in the positive or the negative states, each endowed with power of attraction for the other and both capable of neutralizing each other by uniting.

As regards man, interaction processes have been developed to an extreme because his sensory mechanisms are so diverse and respond to such a wide-ranging wave spectrum. Sight, hearing, smell, touch, and, above all, speech refine the forms of remote action. In sexual mechanisms nature has developed prodigies of genius, all of which tend to ensure its full efficiency. But the whole range of interactions is far broader than the wavelength of sexual attraction: friendship, love, the urge for possession or pleasure, submission to a god or to a leader, and all forms of concupiscence are their most familiar modalities.

Economics studies the effect of interactions based on the desire for wealth, just as physics studies the effect of electric or magnetic interactions. In economic theory the particle is man. Like the wave associated with a corpuscle, at each instant his desire ranges over the whole of his economic space and realizes itself in "demands" of a specific size, depending upon the desirable corpuscles it encounters. The description of a wave in terms of wave mechanics is easily applicable, *mutatis mutandis*, to the wave of desire in economics. In Broglie's words:

> the corpuscle may be thought of as guided by the wave, which plays the part of a pilot wave. . . . Thus viewed, the wave in no way represents a physical phenomenon occurring in any region of space; it is, rather, a mere symbolical representation of what we know about the corpuscle. . . . There are two complementary aspects of reality: space-time localization, and dynamic specification in terms of energy and quantity of movement. . . . The presence of a corpuscle changes the properties of all the space around it; in other words, the corpuscle is only the center of an extended phenomenon.[18]

Obviously, in any given economic space, individual supplies and demands can be summed to yield the aggregates that economic theory deals with. But it would distort the analogy to search for any representational or objective identity in such aggregates. They simply portray a structural community for which, in physics as in economics, the microscopic and the macroscopic are two complementary systems of explanation. Above all, this analogy leads to the realization that "when we move up to the macroscopic world, the discontinuous nature of these individual phenomena disappears, drowned as it were in the statistical reality."[19]

This parallel is even borne out by Heisenberg's concept of indeterminacy:

> The corpuscle may be considered, in one sense, "free" to manifest itself here or there, with varying energy levels [Do not these words recall the liberty of economic choice, which generates unforeseeable supplies and demands?];

---

[18] Ibid., pp. 186–187.
[19] Ibid., p. 260.

but, given initial data, we can calculate exactly the probability that it will make one choice rather than another. This last remark is reminiscent of the statistical determination of economic phenomena. It leads to a conclusion which applies equally to economics and physics: "The apparent determinism in macroscopic phenomena does not conflict with the notions of the new mechanics which is based essentially on the wave-corpuscle complementarity."[20]

Thus the fundamental unity of the scientific interpretation of our universe within the diversity of the natural sciences is made clear.

The integration of individuals into society

The confrontation of the concepts of private individual and corporate bodies—i.e. the concepts of individual, in the strict sense of the word, and society—poses difficult problems to the lawyer, the economist, or the sociologist. It is important to note that the physicist has had to face the same problems. Louis de Broglie says:

> It is indisputable that in a great number of phenomena we can distinguish physical units. . . . The concept of physical individual is therefore roughly applicable to reality. But if we wish to define it with rigor, we find that we have to consider a unit completely isolated from the rest of the world. The moment several units begin to interact among themselves, the individuality of each one is somehow reduced. This fact can even be observed in classical physics. The old theories symbolized the actions and reactions of physical units, and calculated their effects, by means of the "potential energy" concept.
> Now the mutual action potential energy belongs to

[20] Ibid., pp. 260 (the words in brackets are mine), 247.

the whole system, and cannot in any logical manner be distributed among the constituents of the system.

Let us take the simple case of two electrified particles reacting on each other; classical physics assigns to each of them a kinetic energy. The total energy of the system formed by the two particles is the sum of their respective kinetic energies plus the potential energy which represents the interaction between the particles, according to Coulomb's law. Now this potential energy cannot be attributed to either one or the other; it belongs to the system they make up. Thus, under classical theories, potential energy reflects—in a way which is both obscure and profound—the dismantlement of individuality suffered by each of the physical units when they enter into interaction.[21]

In another book, the same author makes the following observation:

in many common cases of this sort, the potential energy of an ensemble of corpuscles is much smaller than the individual energies of each of them. But the notion of individual mass must certainly lose its validity where interactions are extremely intense. Hence the conclusion that the individuality of the elementary corpuscles is all the weaker as they are more thoroughly caught up in the bonds of interaction.[22]

This finding applies as much to the soldier caught up in the bonds of interaction which pertain to military discipline, or to the Jesuit whose personality is checked by the demands of his order, as it does to an atom or an electron enclosed within the powerful structures of a molecule or an atom.

---

[21] Ibid., p. 278.

[22] Louis de Broglie, *Continu et discontinu en physique quantique*, 1941, p. 116.

The physicist's analysis sheds light on the problems with which the economist and the sociologist are concerned when they oppose individualism and socialism, or even collectivism and totalitarianism. No one who has grasped the distinction between kinetic energy—which is characteristic of each particle—and potential energy—which is characteristic of the system—can doubt the contingency of social forms. The individual continues to exist only insofar as he is not caught up in unduly strong bonds of interaction. To the extent that these grow more efficacious, individuality is attenuated. It can vanish almost altogether in the closely integrated societies of totalitarian systems or of religious orders subject to a very strict discipline.

The practical conclusion applies as much to the physical as to the human sciences:

> Because no corpuscle is completely isolated and because, on the other hand, the combination of corpuscles in a system is virtually never so complete as to leave no trace of their individualities, we see that, on the whole, reality seems to be an intermediate stage between the concept of completely autonomous individuality and the concept of a fully coalesced system.[23]

I hope that this lesson will not be lost to policy makers, economists, and sociologists. It can reduce the differences between them by teaching them that where they see irreconcilable conflicts of doctrine there is nothing more than varying degrees of integration. Even the sterile controversies about federation vs. confederation, nationality vs. supranationality, can be viewed more clearly in the light of quantum mechanics.

It is disheartening to realize that experts in the human sciences had to wait for the progress of quantum mechanics to

23 Ibid.

clarify their problems. They could long ago have followed the reverse process and analyzed structures with which they were quite familiar. Thus extremely valuable light would have been shed on the characteristics of atomic or molecular structures as well as the cellular societies constituted of living beings.

Complementarity and idealization

The foregoing analysis underscores the impossibility of explaining reality without relying on two causal series, one relating to the existence of corpuscles and the other to the existence of waves. The two series are "complementary" in that each of them "explains" one part of the phenomena observed, while the whole would remain inexplicable if both were not used simultaneously. They are complementary but mutually exclusive, in that each of them is more closely adapted to certain aspects of reality as the other is less so adjusted, and vice versa.

Niels Bohr, the great physicist, was the first to demonstrate the importance of complementarity in theoretical physics by opposing the concept of individualized unit to that of a system:

> In quantum physics, a system is a kind of organism within whose unity the elementary constituent units are almost totally absorbed. When it forms part of a system, a physical unit loses in it a large measure of its individuality, as the latter tends to merge into the greater individuality of the system. . . .
>
> To individualize a physical unit which is part of a system, it is necessary to sever this unit from the system, to break the link that binds it to the total organism. Thus we can understand in what way the concepts of individual unity and system are complementary, the particle being unobservable while it is geared to the system, and the

system being disrupted the moment the particle has been identified. Therefore the concept of physical unit is perfectly clear and well defined only to the extent that one deals with a unit entirely independent of the rest of the world; but, as such independence is clearly not feasible, the concept of physical unit considered in its full purity appears in its turn as an idealization, a case which never completely fits in with reality.

Furthermore, the same thing applies to the concept of system. Strictly defined, a system is an entirely self contained organism totally unrelated to the outside world: strictly speaking, therefore, the concept can only relate to the entire universe.[24]

When we read these lines, can we doubt that they apply as much to societies of men as to societies of corpuscles?

To human reason, the principle of complementarity is an acknowledgment of defeat. Indeed, this principle is a mere statement of a basic fact: when set forth in loose form, the conceptions of our minds are, by and large, applicable to reality; but if we refine them to an extreme, they become ideal forms whose real content is evanescent. "The success of physical theory has proven the possibility of accommodating, at least roughly, a good many categories of phenomena within the framework of certain logical schemes constructed by human reason. This global fitting in of reality and human reason is, in a sense, truly marvelous." But the dual explanation involved in the principle of complementarity demonstrates that such correspondence exists only within certain limits of precision. When the sophistication of our methods of observation pinpoints the details of phenomena, it no longer seems possible to maintain an unequivocal correspondence between all the characteristics observed and a perfectly defined logical scheme. "Is it certain," de Broglie concludes, "that the static

[24] *Matter and Light*, p. 279.

concepts of our reason, with their clearcut and bare outlines, can be applied to and perfectly fit a moving and infinitely complex reality?"[25]

It is significant, considering the purport of this discussion, that in this same work the renowned physicist found that the conclusions to which he had been led by studying physical phenomena could be extended to the human sciences, at least in general terms:

> In the psychological, moral, or social sphere, extremely rigorous definition or reasoning is often misleading and does not afford guidance in the study of reality. Facts, no doubt, tend to array themselves in accordance with formats provided by our reason; but that is no more than a tendency, and the facts always overflow if the framework is too exactly defined.
>
> Thus, in the rather unprecise sphere of the human sciences, the strictness of the definitions varies inversely to their degree of applicability to the real world. But are we justified in comparing this fact with the circumstances encountered during the development of modern physics? We are, it is true, dealing here with an analogy whose implications must not be exaggerated; but I think that it is less superficial than one might at first believe. Whenever we want to describe the facts, whether in the psychological or in the moral field, or in the sphere of physical and natural sciences, we are always faced with two things that must be confronted and to the greatest extent possible reconciled: reality which is always infinitely complex and comprises an infinity of nuances, on the one hand, and our understanding, which conceptualizes more or less rigidly and schematically, on the other. There is no doubt that our concepts are capable of adjusting to reality to a large extent, if we leave them

[25] Ibid., p. 275.

a certain margin of indetermination; otherwise, no argument relating to reality could be marshalled in any context whatsoever. But it is more doubtful whether such adequation can be maintained throughout if we insist on eliminating any margin of indetermination and refining our concepts to the extreme. Even in the most exact of natural sciences—physics—the need for margins of indetermination has become clear, and that is a fact, it seems to me, that should attract the attention of philosophers, because it may throw new light on the way in which the idealizations formed by our reason agree with reality.[26]

The above remarks are essential. I shall need to refer to them in the closing chapters of this book, where I attempt an interpretation of the order which characterizes our universe.

Postscript to Chapter II

Having relied so heavily on Louis de Broglie's views, I must, in all loyalty to him, call attention to the evolution which his present thinking betokens. In *Certitudes et incertitudes de la science*, he writes as follows:

> I am profoundly convinced that there is a physical reality which exists outside us and is independent of our thought and our imperfect means of knowing it. . . . I also believe in the need to base our theories about physical phenomena . . . on precise pictures of their evolution in time and space. . . . On balance, the search for the causality which links successive phenomena has always been and remains the surest guide to scientific research. . . .
>
> What does it mean to assert that the position of a particle is uncertain? Does it mean that at every instant the particle has a position but that we do not know it, or rather

[26] Ibid., p. 281.

58

that the position of the particle, in the whole area, is really indeterminate, that it is somehow "ubiquitous"? . . . For my part, I think that a physical magnitude always has, in reality, a specific value. That is why I am today led to believe that one ought to be very cautious in the face of the statement—so often repeated by physicists during the last forty years or so—that transitional quantum phenomena would, to use an expression of Nils Bohr, transcend any description in terms of time and space, and would, as a result, be definitely incomprehensible. My conclusion will therefore be that present-day interpretations of quantum physics ought in future to be replaced by theoretical notions which will provide more complete and clearer pictures of microphysical reality. [27]

I cannot pass judgement on the theoretical basis (the dual solution theory and the hidden thermodynamics of particles) which brought about a new orientation in the thinking of the creator of wave mechanics. I might perhaps be permitted, however, to observe that, in the light of the considerations developed in the preceding chapter and in view of the widespread nature of the concepts of individual and interaction—as well as the indeterminacy that characterizes individual behavior when the individual is a human person—present-day interpretations of quantum physics, especially Heisenberg's uncertainty principle, do not appear as surprising as they seemed at first blush.

Perhaps the strength of the synthesis I am attempting lies in the fact that particulate indeterminacy provides a glimpse into a general characteristic of nature when viewed not in its statistical aspects but on the level of the individual, regardless of his place in the hierarchy of societies that constitute the universe.

[27] Louis de Broglie, *Certitudes et incertitudes de la science*, pp. 44–45.

CHAPTER III

The Attrition of Structures and the Increase in Entropy

A social order is never spontaneous

THE PRECEDING CHAPTER demonstrated that an "order" is never a spontaneous phenomenon: it is always produced by the coordination of a certain amount of individual behavior. Such coordination can result only from interactions between the individuals it binds together or between each of these individuals and one individual in a dominant position. So long as such interactions are firm, they generate and sustain a social order. But the moment they weaken, the order slackens. If they cease altogether, i.e. if they no longer have an effective influence on individual behavior, the individuals regain their independence and the order disappears altogether.

Thus the society formed by a mother cat and her kittens disappears with the interaction that arises between them during nursing, no doubt as a psychological effect of the hormones associated with the lactation process. The cat and her kittens then become independent of one another. Similarly, an electron that has been released from the atomic structure to which it belonged becomes an independent individual. As a result of its own characteristics, and under no other influence, it traces out its own lifeline, which is in fact its path.

60

Thus a social structure which generates existence is never spontaneous but is always the improbable outcome of the interactions that tend to bring it about.

The hierarchy of structures

An individual released from a social order does not necessarily become independent, however. It can be—and, indeed, generally is—caught up by interactions which remained under dominance so long as those which generated the previously existing social order retained their full sway. These interactions become dominant as soon as the latter lose some or all of their efficaciousness.

Thus an electron released from an atom can be captured by another proton if its path comes so close that the resulting interaction will nullify its momentum. Similarly, the rocks and dust resulting from the erosion and decay of a mountain can be caught up by terrestrial gravity and, along with our planet itself, constitute, in the form of sediment, a new order which is less complex than the one to which they previously belonged. This is the fate of all bodies subject to gravity when they are released from a social order. Having been grasped by the gravitational field which has become dominant, they join the dust of ruins and the remains of all living creatures, becoming part of a very simple order, that of cemeteries.

The attrition of interactions

It is a fact that, in our world, no interaction is everlasting. Interactions gradually weaken and slacken, where they do not suddenly disappear altogether, as the result of some accident. This is the message Ecclesiastes conveys when he reminds us that all are of the dust and shall turn to dust again.

The decay of interactions is effected according to very differing processes. It may be the result of gradual erosion, such as that which wind and rain work on the order mountains constitute; it may be the direct consequence of the functioning of an organism, some of whose own by-products can have corrosive or disrupting effects—causing, for instance, sclerosis or arthritis. It may even be the outcome of chance encounters which produce accidents, like those collisions whose impact destroys atomic structures.

Nor do political, social, and even religious doctrines, the foundations of those orders characteristic of human society, escape the attrition of time. Under the influence of the evolution of ideas, of the oppositions they give rise to, and of the growth of rival creeds, they gradually lose their efficacy vis-à-vis the behavior they govern; the bonds which were the essence of the social order they had created weaken. Thus "under the sun . . . all is vanity and vexation of spirit." All such structures—like those of radioactive atoms—remain precarious and inevitably doomed to undergo the process of disruption which will terminate their "existence."

The most probable state is the final term of the evolution of all systems

Because all structures are fated to disappear through the gradual decay of the interactions that generated them, their constituent particles will eventually recover their independence—at least to the extent that they are not so numerous or so close to one another that effective and lasting interactions will be established between them. In fact, "every ensemble formed of a great number of elements which are independent of one another and exchange energy . . . necessarily tends toward states in which energy and matter are distributed over space in a statistically uniform manner." This tendency toward uniformity, toward the absence of any particular arrangement—i.e. of any "order"—is the necessary consequence of independence. Indeed, independence implies "the absence of any influence that could possibly affect the evolution of the system and might have a preference for specific states or groups of states."[1]

This finding involves the notion of entropy. In his work on thermodynamics, Clausius defined entropy as a value which, in a mass of gas, measures the degree of disorder of its molecules, and declared that "while the energy of an isolated system remains constant, its entropy is constantly increasing." At bottom, the law of the increase of entropy is nothing more than statement of the irreversible tendency of such a system to evolve "toward a state characterized by the complete disarray of its constituent elements."[2]

However, Claussius's assertion, in his famous memorandum on "the mechanical theory of heat," that the entropy of the universe was constantly tending toward a maximum, was a bold, if not rash, generalization. Indeed, it is valid only as regards isolated systems composed of mutually independent elements. Such a structure is in fact only a final term, the outcome of the almost complete liberty of its elemental particles. In nature, there are few truly free individuals—i.e. individuals not situated in a "field" which orientates their action—except perhaps in cosmic space.

Nevertheless,

> if out of all possible states we count those which evidence particular characteristics, that is to say a certain degree of order, and those about which we have nothing to say, which are uniform in their disorder, we find immediately that the second category is infinitely greater than the

[1] Pierre Auger, *L'Homme microscopique*, 1952, pp. 28, 29.
[2] Brunold, *L'Entropie*, pp. 100, 197.

first. The states of disorder are like an ocean on which float tiny islets of order. . . . The chances of reaching one of them, at random, are virtually nil. Besides, if some influence should happen to array the system into an improbable state of order, we should only have to wait for it eventually to fall back into disorder.

It is clear that the above considerations about probability do not demonstrate the impossibility, in the absolute sense of the word, of the spontaneous appearance of an orderly state evolved from a system in uniform disorder. Such a spontaneous emergence simply becomes less and less probable as the number of independent particles increases. If, like the universe, the system comprises a very high number of particles, the improbability, in fact, amounts to an impossibility.[3]

And yet we can find all around us orders which are infinitely complex, whose degrees of probability are therefore almost nil. There is a human being, for example, or the combination of words constituting Pascal's *Pensées,* or the combination of notes which make up Beethoven's Fifth Symphony. Since such orders cannot be spontaneous or fortuitous, they must be the result of a process whose tendency it is to bring them about. It is the principle inherent in such a process that we shall examine in the next chapter.

[3] Auger, *L'Homme microscopique,* p. 30.

CHAPTER IV

Against the Stream: the Ascent of Order

The passion of the Gods; the increase in entropy

THE TRAGIC FACT about order is that, once established, it tends to melt like snow in the sun. Hence all creation is unstable because, unavoidably, its constitutive order will gradually disintegrate as its various parts revert to the most probable state, in which they will regain stability and endurance. Thus, "every portion of our universe, and perhaps even our entire universe itself, would appear to be doomed to perish in a sort of general indifference." [1]

If this tendency applied to a quantity of order established once and for all—that is to say, a nonrenewable "creation"—our world, carried away by a stream of increasing entropy, would drift inevitably toward thermal death and the nondifferentiated state which would reflect it. All "organization," being fated to disappear, would soon disappear.

But this is not in fact the case. On the contrary, history reveals a progressive accumulation of increasingly complex orders. The evolution of living species, the appearance over time of beings more and more highly organized and provided with increasingly refined vital mechanisms, the development

---

[1] Pierre Auger, *L'Homme microscopique*, p. 28.

of human creations—factories, cities, states, armies, sophisticated machinery comprising innumerable parts, mathematical or physical theories, more and more subtle poems and symphonies—all betoken an ascent of order which gradually spreads, organizes an ever increasing number of particles, and encloses them within more and more complex structures.

There is no doubt that the two currents coexist. One feeds on the other—since, as Carnot's principle puts it, whenever order appears, its emergence is accompanied by an increase in disorder. But the current generative of order is carrying our world along toward levels of organization that are more and more highly differentiated. Thus it constantly lifts the world back out of the abyss of uniformity in which it would tend to founder if left to itself.

All existing orders are possible, but they are only a very small part of all the possibilities

All existing orders have been established and are maintained by interactions. Each of them is the "development" of forms that were potentially contained in the sum of particles composing it and in the interactions that have the power to unite them. An order opens out like those Japanese water flowers people used to give to children when they had been good (I do not know whether this is still done). As soon as these tiny spheres of paper were put in water, they spread into fascinating patterns. The appearance of these complex structures came as a surprise; but it is clear that they were present in the seed and that contact with water had caused them to spring forth.

Similarly, each "form" preexists in the collectivity of its constituent particles. But it will not be realized unless those interactions that bind them are effectively established and reach the level of intensity at which they will control individual behavior. The intensity of interactions generally depends on the distance separating the particles from one another. An electron must pass quite close to a proton to be captured by it; a male and female cannot form a couple until they encounter.

But the "personality" of each of these constituent particles is protected by the discontinuities separating it from all its fellows. Whether it be a defense against one of its own kind, against egotism, or against the rim of a potential well, the "wall of private life" tends to protect a being against any violation of its individuality or control by a higher order. If individuality were not protected, it would not endure.

Potential interactions cannot generate an existent unless they succeed in overcoming obstacles and hostile forces. If an electron is to join an atomic society, for example, its speed must be great enough to enable it to penetrate the potential well enclosing the atom but not so great that it can move out after penetration.

In general, a new order is established by the accretion of particles of matter and energy to an already existing structure. The growth of complexity is now known to be endothermic phenomenon, characterized by an accumulation of potential energy within the existent. At the opposite extreme, the destruction of an order—like combustion or nuclear disintegration—is an exothermic phenomenon. Thus we can view creation as the storing up of matter and energy in new structures since matter itself is nothing more than condensed energy, this accumulation process prevents the dissipation of energy into cosmic infinities. Hence a potential order can truly come into existence only if the many complex conditions prerequisite to its materialization are all met at the same time.

The materialization of an order causes new interactions to appear, however, and thus a new gamut of possibilities. It is among such possibilities that the choices that spell history will be effected, depending upon unforeseeable encounters.

The number of possibilities increases constantly with the complexity of possibilities already realized. The moment a possibility has been endowed with existence, it offers evolution a new field of potentialities, in which reality will eventually be reaped.

Every creator has his own machines

An order is always improbable. If it is to "exist," it must not only be possible, i.e. amenable to being maintained by effective interactions, but also materialize effectively. And it will do so when particles, provided with adequate energy, are actually located in a manner that gives rise to those interactions which will confer both stability and endurance upon the society thus generated.

Theoretically, it is not impossible that, as the result of an extraordinary set of contingencies, all the circumstances required to bring about an enduring pattern may sometimes be met. One can, for example, imagine that after an avalanche two large rocks happen to be placed on top of one another in such a way that gravity will turn this ensemble into a long-lasting association. Furthermore, another avalanche might superimpose a third stone upon this ensemble, and so on, until, after a very long period of time, a series of fortuitous and varying events had erected an actual house. But the least that can be said is that no one has ever seen a house erected through such a process. And it is unlikely, if not entirely out of the question, that any will ever be.

Anyone who actually wants to "create" the particular arrangement of stones called a house first carries them to the building site and then uses a winch to lift each one to a level where positioning them on top of one another will, with the assistance of gravity, bring about those interactions that will confer stability upon the new society thus formed. The winch which transforms the human or chemical energy it receives (whether it is hand- or motor-operated) has imparted to the two stones making up an ensemble, by means of a transfer, the potential energy necessary for the establishment of the resulting society. At the same time, it has positioned those two stones in a relation to each other which generates the interaction that binds them together. In this process the winch functions as a "machine": it systematically brings about a pattern which generates a lasting order by "pumping" from outside the energy which the establishment of this order requires; at the same time, however, it remains unchanged, even after the transformation it has wrought is complete. Thus, the machine controls particles of existence as it impels them into a new order.

More generally, the term "machine" is applied to any instrument that can effect a given transformation without being disrupted by that transformation. In this sense, a machine, by controlling particles of existence, is really an order-creating device. If we consider those "orders" that make up our universe, we find that they are always the product of a machine—at least once we learn how they came into existence. An automobile, for instance, is not the result of a random arrangement of parts, but the outcome of an assembly plan effected by suitable machines. Similarly, each part is not the outcome of fortuitous events influencing its components, but the product of the operation of industrial machines specifically designed for that purpose.

A living being is an arrangement of very complicated machines. As such, it is never the result of random events, but the product of that subtle piece of machinery we call an ovum. Our knowledge of the "organizing" mechanisms of the ovum is incomplete. We have, however, learned enough to identify them in terms of a process whereby matter and energy are carefully arrayed according to an unchanging blueprint. It is as if this were done by the most advanced automated machine. The complex machinery produced by the ovum includes, among other machines, a machine for reproducing the machinery, something similar to those produced by factories which manufacture machine tools.

Inanimate orders are, no less than living orders, the products of appropriate machinery. The view is generally held that the large molecules of DNA are self-reproductive; that is, they have the power to control the molecules of a specific substratum in such a way as to organize them into chains analogous to their own. Their activity is similar to that of machine tools, which by assembling parts all day long confer existence upon the finished product which is the purpose of their operation. Metabolism, which enables an animal or a plant to create its own substance out of the diverse elements it finds in its food, is the product of the same type of assembly process.

Chlorophyll provides the most characteristic example of a molecule-machine. It assembles atoms of carbon, oxygen, hydrogen, and nitrogen, along with photons, or particles of light energy, and develops the organic products which are the fabric of living matter. Our understanding of the process of the photosynthesis performed by the molecule of chlorophyll is still incomplete. But we do know that carbon, oxygen, and hydrogen are extracted from carbonic gas and water vapor in the atmosphere, and nitrogen from certain compounds in the soil. The energy necessary to break down the carbonic gas comes from solar radiation.

Thus each green leaf is a miniature factory where innumerable molecule-machines are busy producing organic matter. Light energy is invested for that purpose in the atomic societies formed by organic molecules. Recent research has indicated that the chlorophyll molecule goes through a cycle of complex reactions with the molecules it decomposes and the atoms it synthesizes.[2] This process is distinguished by the fact that

[2] See International Symposium on Photosynthesis, July 23–27, 1962.

the chlorophyll molecule remains intact at the end of the transformation it achieves and can repeat the process indefinitely. This stability, which makes chlorophyll a genuine machine, transforms all the green canopies of the world into one enormous atomic, photosynthetic plant.

"Catalysis" is the term generally used to describe the transformations effected by molecule-machines. Catalytic reactions are countless. Faraday discovered them during the last century, when he demonstrated the action of platinum sponge on a mixture of hydrogen and oxygen. Industry uses it a great deal—in the manufacture of sulphuric acid, for example, or ammonia. Catalytic action is also the basis of the assimilation by means of which living organisms transform into their own substance the food they receive from outside themselves.

It is evident that the catalytic reactions which impose a determined order on constituent particles are merely one particular instance of the existence of control systems: enzymes, for example, bring their constituent elements under control by imposing a new structure upon them. It may be, Norbert Wiener says, that enzymes are machines operating like "Maxwell's devils" to reduce entropy. If that is true, a single human organism encompasses within itself more machines than are to be found in all the factories of the world.

But control systems do not act only at the molecular level. According to the most recent conceptions of atomic structure, which will be summarized in Chapter 5, an atom is essentially a structure which uses control mechanisms to place particles of energy in the "cells" assigned to them by the formal mathematics of quantum mechanics. Thus, the atom, like the molecule, generates order. It cannot, of course, be called a catalyst, because it does not remain unchanged after it has effected all the arrangements, but it does contain a series of potential forms and it stimulates their progressive realization by a gradual process of completion. From this point of view, while not precisely a "machine," it is an instrument of social

71

ordering which prevents the dispersion in space of the particles of energy it brings under control. A fuller knowledge of intranuclear processes would probably lead to similar conclusions concerning the nucleus.

All these considerations demonstrate that the creation, out of the fundamental particles, of all the orders which generate existence is never the outcome of some divine *fiat lux*. In every case, it is clearly the result of the arrangement of particles belonging to the next lower level, which is worked out by adequate instruments. These—i.e. the machines and catalysts which impose structures while they themselves remain unaffected, or the atoms or atomic nuclei which are incorporated into the new structure—develop the potential order they carry within themselves.

One might be tempted to draw metaphysical conclusions from the fact that order in our universe is always formed in appropriate matrices. Such a conclusion would be entirely groundless, however. The existence of matrices of order by no means settles the problem of prime causes. It merely postpones the issue by raising the question of the cause of causes: the influence responsible for the formation of the matrices. That is the major problem, and we shall raise it, without solving it, in the last part of this book. There we shall see that the question of the cause of causes will probably never be resolved.

PART II

Jupiter

There is a story about the president of a women's club in the United States calling a major meeting to order. Before the group could take up the first item on the agenda, which dealt with children's education, she claimed it would have to settle the question of the existence of God. Therefore, she proposed that the first ten minutes be devoted to the discussion of that important matter.

I trust the reader will not consider the title of the second part of this book a similar invitation. The title makes no pretence of settling the matter—even inadvertantly. It is a bald statement of the fact that the world exists and that man, in his desperate quest for an explanation, has imposed on it the principle of sufficient reason: "Whatever exists has a rationale."

The world is a huge accumulation of highly varied orders, whose common characteristic is that they are all improbable. Among all these orders, however, there are some whose cause is perfectly clear to us: they are those that have been "created" by men, who desired their creation and knew that they could effect it. The houses we live in, our automobiles, the industrial or agricultural undertakings which produce the wealth we desire, the cities which meet our common needs, the states which protect us—all these exist because we want them to exist.

But the structures willed into existence by man are little more than tiny islands in the immense range of orders that constitute our universe. Agriculture yields the desired crops and livestock, but the plants and animals that covered the earth before man's intervention are orders no less improbable; and we had nothing whatever to do with their creation. Industry manufactures chemical products difficult to obtain and sophisticated electronic machinery, but Nature, that vast chlorophyll factory, turns out huge quantities of carbohydrates;

75

and we have nothing to do with their creation. Our factories, our cities, our states are all complex structures, planned and organized by ourselves with a view to the services they can render, but the societies of ants and of bees are no less complex, not any less efficient; and we have nothing to do with their creation.

We are not prepared to admit that all these orders, which are at least as improbable as those we have desired, but for which we have no responsibility, do not also have a rationale—a raison d'être. *If nothing else, it might be the irrational reason we call chance.*

In this context "Jupiter" will provide that raison d'être *temporarily. I know that some will call me to account for an apparent prejudgment on the insoluble problem of prime causes. I may even seem to have accepted a transcendental solution of the least subtle sort. Others, on the other hand, will criticize me for lacking the reverence which is required when dealing with revealed truths that correspond to the fundamental religious sense of nearly all human beings.*

I hope both sides will bear with me. I have no intention of evading the issue. And I certainly am not so presumptuous as to propose a solution. For my part, I believe that, in the present state of our knowledge, and possibly for all time, perhaps even because of the essential characteristic of human thought, the problem does not fall within the purview of discursive reasoning. It is capable only of individual solutions, selected for reasons which are hardly rational.

In the last part of this book I shall state, as a matter of courtesy to both sides, not what I know but what I personally believe. Until that time, I trust that the reader will understand that the term I use to introduce this second part of the book represents one of the unknowns in the great problem posed by the existence of order in the universe. Part III will introduce yet another of these unknowns. And it is by bringing them closer together that I shall try to make clear, in my conclusion, not merely the extent of our knowledge but also the depth of our ignorance and the reasons for our humility.

CHAPTER V

A Summary of Jupiterian Evolution

T HE JUPITERIAN ORDER—the order not willed into existence by man—is divided into a certain number of increasingly complex "levels of organization." Furthermore, each level also comprises increasingly complex structures.

Energy, the raw material of the universe

The present state of our knowledge of the structure of fundamental particles has not as yet enabled us to identify any feature common to all of them. Louis de Broglie, however, worked out a tentative synthesis based on a set of assumptions. In order to avoid exaggerating the scope of this attempt, I shall simply quote Broglie himself:

> Giving free rein to our imagination, we could suppose that at the beginning of time, on the morrow of some divine *fiat lux*, light, at first alone in the world, gradually

77

produced, by a process of gradual condensation, the physical universe such as, thanks to light, we can contemplate it today. . . .

The union of the concepts of light and of matter is effected in this protean entity we call energy. It was completely proved by the progress of modern physics on the day when it discovered that particles of matter are liable to disappear as they give rise to radiation, while on the other hand radiation can condense into matter and create new particles.

Thus it is that two electrons of opposite signs (the standard negative electron and the positive electron, or positron) can annihilate each other; this dematerialization of a pair of electrons, which is consistent with the principle of the conservation of electricity (since two equal charges of opposite sign disappear at the same time), is accompanied by the emission of two photons of radiation, so that the energy of the two electrons reappears in its entirety in the form of radiating energy. In the process, energy assumes a different form but fully conserves itself, simply changing from matter to light. Conversely, in favorable circumstances, a photon can give rise to a pair of electrons of contrary sign; in this case, again, energy and electricity are conserved, but the energy of light has been converted into matter.

All these facts clearly prove that matter and light are merely different modalities of energy, which can take on successively one or the other of these two appearances.

What characterizes light in the whole gamut of the manifestations of energy is that it is the fastest, the most refined, of all such manifestations. . . .

Carrying with it no perceptible mass and no electron charge, it goes its way endlessly through space without requiring any medium, and physicists see in it, with their mind's eye, a conveyance of the electromagnetic field in its purest form. . . .

In short, light is the most subtle form of matter.[1]

The binary foundation of existence

Left to themselves, photons would have been dispersed in space according to their individual speeds. Nothing could ever have existed.

In certain circumstances, however, a photon may break down into a pair of electrons of contrary signs. This decomposition radically transforms the universe in which it occurs. Previously, there were only neutral individuals which were therefore unable to enter into association. Their existence alone exhausted all the possibilities of creation.

On the other hand, electrons and protons are capable of interactions among themselves because of their respectively negative and positive characteristics. Thus they are social individuals able to generate durable structures, which is not true of photons.

It is their sensitivity to external influences that endows electrically charged particles with the capacity to enter into a society. This ability effectively introduced into our universe the seeds of development and opened up all the avenues of evolution and progress.

Although interactions among particles charged with electricity of opposite signs are the most familiar examples, they are not the sole bonds of social orders. Within the nucleus, for example, there are what might be called "exchange forces." Each level of organization seems to be characterized by the emergence of a specific type of interaction. Forces, attractions, tropisms, appetites, needs, desire, love, and all the various forms of concupiscence are the main varieties.

The interactions among living beings as individuals, which

[1] Louis de Broglie, *Physics and Microphysics*, pp. 69, 68.

are administered by specialized sensory organs, evidence a high degree of diversity and complexity.

But interaction—such as that between positive and negative electrical charges—is nearly always binary in nature. Particles are divided into two different "sexes" at each level of organization; this distribution is the basis of every social grouping. Economic societies themselves are under the binding influence of interactions between buyers and sellers, demanders and suppliers.

Nature uses her resources sparingly. With the process of interaction between negative and positive electrical charges available to her, she appears to have extended its use.

This viewpoint encompasses the whole universe of conclusions François Jacob derived from the study of biological phenomena alone. Little by little, after 1930,

> biologists came to realize that, despite the diversity of organisms, the whole living world used the same materials to effect similar reactions. . . . Quite unexpectedly, they found that frequently there was only one and the same solution for all living beings. There was no escaping the conclusion that Nature, having once found the solution which was to prove best, held on to it during the whole process of evolution.[2]

It would seem that the creator, once he had proved the efficacy of a procedure, had secured a patent on it so that he could use it whenever it might serve his purpose.

But this anthropomorphic language will arouse sarcasm and criticism in many of my readers. I agree with them in advance and again ask them to regard such phrases as the weakness of a mind which is apt to generalize. Unfortunately, it has long moved away from the austerity of scientific thinking.

[2] Inaugural lecture, May 7, 1965, College de France, in *Cahiers de l'Institut de la Vie*, July 1966.

The level of fundamental particles

At present there are about one hundred known fundamental particles, among which electrons, protons, and neutrons rank foremost. All these particles are defined by their energy. The vicissitudes of their existence—and, in particular, its enduring nature—the circumstances leading to their appearance, disappearance, and transformation are such that one can regard them as societies made up of particles of light, or photons.

Neutrons and protons are thought to be two forms of the same elementary particle, called the nucleon. The passage from the proton state to the neutron state is just as possible as the reverse process. There is at present no general theory regarding fundamental particles, however, and we are reduced to mere hypotheses like, for example, the one stated earlier.

The nuclear level

Atomic nuclei are structures made up of protons and neutrons. Beginning with the single proton of the hydrogen nucleus, their numbers increase. Knowledge of the nucleus was greatly enlarged by the study of the spontaneous or induced transmutations to which it can give rise. Such transmutations are the result of the bombardment of the nuclear structure by particles hurling at great speed.

Research has indicated that the nucleus can be regarded as a "potential well" containing protons and neutrons at certain energy levels. So long as these particles remain within the nucleus, they are maintained there; as soon as they emerge from it, they are violently repelled. Thus the nucleus maintains within its structure the particles of energy which form its own substance. The latter either "belong" or do not; there is no halfway state.

As a consequence, the nucleus is separated from the rest

of the world by a discontinuum and is therefore a genuine individual. As such, it constitutes an enduring order which brings under its control individuals belonging to the next lower level. It prevents the scattering over space which would occur were those individuals not solidly confined within a nuclear society.

Our knowledge of the nature of proton-neutron interactions —which takes place at distances of about 10^{-13} centimeters—is still inadequate. Nor do we understand why the proton carries the positive charge, although the electron, which bears the negative charge, has a mass some 2,000 times smaller. It seems that the electrical charges of the particles play only an ancillary role in the stability of the nucleus. Thus intranuclear forces are of a completely different type from macroscopic forces or those at work in the electron layers of the atom. But we have not yet developed a precise formulation of these forces.

On the other hand, the properties of the nucleus, its extent, mass, charge, the binding energy of its constituents, its energy level and degree of stability, are all well known.

The atomic level

The system of nuclear arrangement has been responsible for practically all the substance of the universe:

> Stellar matter is in fact a quasi-nuclear gas formed of very small atomic nuclei, stripped of most of their electrons by high temperatures and radiation and accompanied by a complementary electron atmosphere; in a word, it is a gas of very small electrically charged particles. . . . Almost all the universe exists in this simple form, at high temperature and under high pressures. Only a tiny quantity of matter, that constituting stellar atmospheres, interstellar matter, and the planets, exists

in the usual and complex form with which we are familiar.[3]

Nuclear gases encompassed an immense population of individuals maintained in an asocial state by the temperature and pressure conditions characteristic of stellar matter. If they had remained in such a state, their energy would have dissipated into space. They would not have brought forth any "existence" other than that which they themselves expressed. If they had fortuitously become concentrated in a limited space, so that many clashes would occur, their ensemble would have tended toward the most probable state, which corresponds to maximum entropy: namely, thermal death. The history of the universe would have come to an end.

However, protons and electrons, the constituent individuals of stellar matter, were "sexed"—i.e. capable of interactions. Changes in temperature and pressure conditions alone could bring such interactions about. Electrons and protons could then associate and, having been brought under proper control, would constitute the individuals of a higher order: atoms.

I shall not attempt to present the history of atomic populations here. To date no cosmogony has won the assent necessary for full credibility. On the other hand, advances in the knowledge of atomic structures have been such that the atom can be regarded as a prodigious instrument for the establishment and propagation of order in the universe.

In the Rutherford-Bohr planetary model, the atom was a small planetary system. Its positive charge was concentrated within a central core, the nucleus, around which the electrons gravitated like planets in the solar system. But this model yielded no explanation of the stability of the atom, or of its emission of radiation.

Niels Bohr filled these gaps by superimposing certain principles of quantification on the planetary model. He declared

[3] A. Dauvilliers, *Cosmologie et chimie*, 1955.

that an atomic structure could not assume all the states of motion but was capable of only certain of them.

He acknowledged, in the first place, that the "moment" defined by a specific amount of movement was quantified; its only values could be whole multiples of a fundamental constant, called Planck's constant. This principle led to the definition of a principal quantum number which established the radii of permitted orbits for electrons.

But the need to explain not only the stability of the atom but also some more subtle phenomena—like the frequencies of the light spectra emitted by the atom—required that four other quantum numbers (azimuth, spin, internal, and magnetic) be considered. It was also conceded that the electron did not radiate so long as it remained on a permitted orbit; instead, it emitted light when, because of the loss of a photon or quantum of light energy, it fell on to another permitted orbit.

In order to move from these principles of quantification to a general atomic theory, it was enough to admit that, within an atom composed of a nucleus and several electrons, the electrons were so arranged that the sum of energy in the system was as small as possible. Furthermore, each possible state, characterized by its four quantum numbers, could be occupied by a single electron only.

One consequence of these principles was that the electrons around their nucleus could occupy only certain well-defined positions, those consistent with their levels of energy. The possible positions constituted four layers, K, L, M, N, with K composed of two levels, L of eight, M of eighteen, and N of thirty-two.

This magnificent synthesis marvelously explained Mendeleyev's periodic table. It was now possible to view the "creation" of matter as the progressive occupation of the various possible states, or the progressive filling up of all possible levels, by electrons. Thus, in terms of our analysis, matter appeared as an incarnation of preexisting "possibles."

The Rutherford-Bohr model, however, was characterized by some purely particulate concepts. The need to take into account phenomena which could only be explained by a wave theory obliged Broglie, Schrödinger, Heisenberg, Pauli, and Dirac, beginning in 1925, to substitute for the planetary atomic theory a number of principles which are the foundation of "wave mechanics" or "quantum mechanics."

This theory foregoes entirely any atomic model. Instead, it puts forth a system of calculations that make it possible to predict the observable properties of atomic structures, especially their spectra. The behavior of each particle, according to quantum mechanics, is determined only by a certain function—ω—called the wave function. This is itself defined by a differential equation known as Schrödinger's equation. Fundamental quantification is thus reintroduced, because Schrödinger's equation has no solution unless the energy (E) of the electron has specific values—that is, values specific to the problem, which are identical to those in Bohr's earlier quantification.

In this system, the electron's paths have no concrete significance. Only the probability that a particle will be in a certain point in space is defined. Atomic properties are no longer determined by the positions of the electrons but by their energy levels.

Because quantum mechanics foregoes predictions of the paths of electrons (since Heisenberg's principle of uncertainty excludes the possibility of knowing simultaneously the speed and position of any single one), it can indicate only that electrons ought to evolve within certain privileged regions of the space around the nucleus, called orbitals. These regions can be regarded as cells which combine to form layers and sublayers.

The imposing structure of quantum mechanics, with all its complexity and abstractions, has a decisive justification in its explanatory capacity. Today, however, considering the

85

present state of science, some investigators, especially Louis de Broglie, question whether the break with the concrete is final. Some new synthesis might make it possible to leave the realm of mathematical entities and revert to the world of objects localized in both time and space.[4]

Whatever may happen in the future, both theories—i.e. the planetary model and quantum mechanics—entail one consequence. They view the atom as a controlling mechanism which subjects particles of energy to specific structures. Whether they are contained in cells or in orbits, these particles relinquish their own behavior to join the atomic order. Both explanations confer upon some structures the privilege of being the only possible ones. They tend to transform "creation" into a process whereby various forms that are capable of existing are gradually filled with particles of energy. Thus the atomic order categorizes particles of energy in the permitted forms, preventing the increase in entropy which would have been inevitable had the protons and electrons remained free.

The complexity of this systematic view increases with the number of particles included—protons, neutrons and electrons. Technically, the atom acts as a sorting machine, tending to introduce increasing doses of order into the universe. This scheme has its limitations, however. Indeed, it has been found that heavy nuclei—like the nucleus of uranium-235 which, with its 92 protons and electrons, includes a total of 235 nucleons—are less and less stable. The slightest impact—a collision with a neutron, for example—is enough to break them apart. Certain heavy elements, like polonium, radium, and uranium, even disintegrate spontaneously, with emission of radiation; thus they cause the natural radioactivity which Henri Becquerel discovered in 1896.

The instability of heavy nuclei limited to 92 the number

---

[4] See Postscript to Chapter II.

of elements that could possibly exist in nature in a durable way. Any nucleus heavier than uranium-235 could not have survived the 5 billion years separating our era from the time when chemical elements were apparently formed through atomic integration. Therefore, the atomic system's orderly scheme was limited in application. The degree of complexity it was capable of engendering could not extend beyond a certain point. Once it had reached the limit of stability of atomic structures, all its creative power was exhausted. Only a new approach—the molecular technique—could do more and better.

The molecular level

If atoms had not been social beings, the world would have reached its final accomplishment with the gradual formation of all the chemical elements. The quality of the order achieved would have been limited to the degree of complexity attained by the highest atomic formations. It quantity would have steadily decreased in proportion to the increase in entropy.

But atoms were both subjects and objects of interaction. As a result, the individuals they constituted were amenable to entering into societies with other individuals of the same nature. In this way, they formed societies belonging to the next higher level: crystals and molecules.

The study of crystalline and molecular structures is recent and has led to a theory even more complex than the one accounting for atomic structures. The most prevalent notions —which are themselves constantly evolving—view crystalline and molecular societies as the result of interactions of the same nature as those responsible for the atom. Chemical compounds are considered systems formed of a great number of atomic nuclei surrounded by "cells" in which the electrons, whose electrical charges generally balance the charges of the nuclei, move. When the electrons gravitating around a nucleus represent a charge inferior or superior to that of the nucleus, their ensemble constitutes an "ion," which is electrically charged. Crystalline societies are generated by the attraction, termed the "ionic bond," among ions of opposite charges.

Molecular structure is simply a generalization of crystalline structure. It results from the fusion into a molecular electron cloud of the electron clouds formed by the valence electrons of several atoms. This feature is the main difference between crystalline and molecular structure: in the former, all the electrons may be linked to particular nuclei; in the latter, some of them are held in common and belong *en bloc* to the molecule. It is in the overlap of electron clouds that contemporary scientists see the origin of molecular interactions. Such overlapping is capable of uniting identical as well as different atoms, while the ionic bond can unite only different atoms.

The atom blocks constituting molecules are organized into characteristic networks. The description of their forms is the special province of stereochemistry. Their pattern and number vary infinitely. As a result, the networks control more and more individuals, grouping them into more and more complex societies. The progressively increasing complexity of the molecular order eventually generates the larger organic molecules, such as those of the amino acids. Their fundamental atoms—carbon, hydrogen, nitrogen, and, possibly, sulphur—are grouped together into characteristic structures. Desoxyribonucleic acid (DNA), for example, is made up of two chains of atoms arranged in a spiral around one common axis; the two chains are linked by bonds of hydrogen or sulphur between the nucleotide bases. According to current thinking, the minimum size of DNA *in vivo* involves 1,000 turns of the spiral, which implies a molecular weight of 6,700,000.

We are all familiar with the long chains constituting plastics. They are made of small groups of atoms, called monomers, which characteristically unite with their like. They are similar to railroad cars which can only be hooked up to identical cars to make up a train. There are roughly twenty fundamental monomers in the amino acids, and they can generate numerous chains. These chains are so many "substances," whose properties vary according to the nature and order of their constituent amino acids.

The wealth and complexity of the gamuts of "possibles" thus established becomes clearer when one notes that, with chains composed of only 9 amino acids chosen from a collection of 20, the number of different structures possible is 512 billion. Diversification relates not only to the composition of the constituent chains, but also to the atomic "bridges," hydrogen or sulphur, which link them. Furthermore, each structure stimulates the emergence of characteristic properties indissolubly associated with it.

Thus one can see the enormous amount of order the molecular "technique" system has generated. Not only, in controlling atoms, does it encompass great quantities of energy in durable structures—the "investing" aspect of the ordering process—but it organizes them into forms whose diversity and complexity are capable of almost unlimited development.

"Be fruitful and multiply"

The unique power of the molecular technique would be underestimated if it were regarded as a mere instrument for more extensive and complex ordering. The molecule is singled out by the fact that in many of its states it not only "is" but "makes" as well.

We have already seen[5] that catalysts are actually machines which "arrange" matter and energy in the molecular objects they produce. Because of this property, catalysts produce order by multiplying in considerable numbers the ordered

[5] See Chapter IV, p. 65.

states for which, like automated machines, they have been programmed.

Pierre Auger, however, considers machines in general, and catalysts in particular, not creators but transformers of order:

> They never allow a quantitative gain in order; that is, they never make a system pass from one total state, presenting a certain probability, to another, less probable, total state. Nevertheless, within the ensemble of a system, certain portions may move into very unusual and improbable states, provided that a new uniformity grows up—compensating for and moving beyond for this localized diminution of probability—in other parts of the system which presented a certain degree of order.[6]

For my part, I am convinced that the operation of both catalysts and machines respects the principle of conservation of energy, and I likewise grant the possibility of a sort of principle of conservation of entropy. Nevertheless, I am reluctant to believe that catalysts, in their controlling activity, merely transform previously existing arrangements and never generate that ill-defined quality which is associated in our minds with the notion of "order."

I know of no precise measurement, if not of the quantity, at least of the quality, of order. Therefore, any stated conservation principle relating to order seems to me—in the present state of our knowledge—to raise almost insuperable difficulties. Until such a principle is formulated, I shall continue to consider it likely that catalysts and machines, when they impose a specific arrangement on particles—in other words, when they control them without any apparent labor—are probably creating order and that they assuredly raise the level of the orders they transform.

The order produced by catalysts and machines remains

[6] Pierre Auger, *L'Homme microscopique*, 1952.

unchangeable as long as they themselves remain unaltered. They reproduce indefinitely the same blueprint, whose plan they thus conserve. On the other hand, with change whatsoever in their interior structure—whether accidental or deliberate—the "product" will be altered. When the duplicating machine is a catalytic molecule, an alteration of a single one of its atoms—for instance, by the chance entrance of an electron—effects a mutation in the product. Biology provides many examples.[7] When the machine is a device by men, every change in its structure changes the product.

Generally speaking, the order produced by catalysts and machines is different from that of which they themselves are the expression. However, one very special instance of the ordering process appears when it reproduces exactly the order of its own producing instrument. Here one encounters the mechanisms of autocatalysis or self-reproduction. Such processes are of supreme importance because they open the way leading to life.

DNA's long molecule possesses the remarkable capacity, when introduced into an appropriate substratum, of controlling the constituent elements and producing a new molecule similar to itself. "Associated with this substratum," says A. Ducrocq, "the molecules of desoxyribonucleic acid may be considered self-reproductive, playing in the algebra of control phenomena the role of identical transformation in the theory of groups."[8] Thus the DNA molecule operates like one of the machines in a machine-tool factory. In producing machines like themselves, they are, in a sense, self-reproductive.

Little is known about the process by which DNA imposes on proteins in its substratum the order which it carries. Observations have shown that each sucrophosphate link in the DNA chain is as long as the links in the amino acids (3.5 angstroms). The fact that they are of the same length clearly aids the

---

[7] See E. Schrödinger, *Qu'est-ce que la vie?*

[8] Ducrocq, *Logique de la vie*, p. 105.

mother-molecule's engagement with the molecules which sustain it.

Pascual Jordan sees multiplication by autocatalysis as the original form of all vital phenomena. It leads to the viruses, whose "personality" synthesizes three characteristics of life: nutrition, growth, and reproduction:

> Each of the fundamental activities of all higher form of life—metabolism and multiplication—is therefore present in the viruses, but in a rudimentary and simplified form: foreign substances are first prepared by the host organism —without which the virus could not exist—and are then transformed by the virus into its own substance. In the light of these characteristics, the virus may be considered a living being.[9]

On the other hand, Stanley and Wyckoff's brilliant experiments have demonstrated that the tobacco mosaic virus is a clearly defined substance, albuminous and crystallizable. Its construction does not vary from one individual to another. Its molecular weight—17,000,000—is always the same, although it is the weight of a society of more than one million atoms. For all these reasons, the virus particle is unquestionably an individual molecule. Thus, Jordan concludes,[10] the virus is the point of contact between the order of living beings and that of molecules.

Because of such catalytic and autocatalytic mechanisms, the molecule is the essential agent responsible for the spread of order through the universe and for the heightening of its level in a process of progressive "complexification." As Stanley, who isolated the crystals of the nucleoprotein responsible for tobacco mosaic, said, the probability of the formation of a material unit by means of simple combination depends upon the chance encounters of the constituent units. The activity

[9] *La Physique et le secret de la vie organique*, pp. 81, 78.
[10] Ibid., p. 79.

of catalytic and autocatalytic molecules obviates this improbability, and when the molecules are themselves provided with an adequate substratum, their power to generate order becomes virtually unlimited.

The level of life organization

I do not believe that there is a clear definition of life. Nor can a clear-cut borderline be established between life and nonlife.

For Jean Rostand, "in the evolution of our globe, the inanimate preceded the animate, and . . . the discovery of protein viruses (one should also add the discovery of bacteriophagi) has notably narrowed the gap between the molecular world and the world of living beings."[11] In the opinion of Pascual Jordan, the lowest level of life and its first beginnings on our planet could very well have been composed of "living molecules—that is, molecules with the ability to reproduce themselves by autocatalysis."[12] F. Nigon's view is that

the evolution moved from macromolecules to the inframicroscopic structures of the cell, then to microsomes, mitochondria, and other cellular organelles, and finally to the cell. . . . Depending upon the requirements formulated for a minimal living being, the limit (between life and nonlife) will be at one level or another in a hierarchy of structures whose activities are becoming more and more diversified as their internal complexity increases.[13]

Jules Carles includes among the specific characteristics of the

[11] Jean Rostand, *Ce que je crois*.
[12] Jordan, op. cit., p. 97.
[13] F. Nigon, "Essai sur la dialectique des origines de la vie," *Cahiers d'études biologiques*, 3, pp. 38–39.

vital process not only structure but also behavior and spontaneity.[14] But we have seen that the atom, the molecule, and especially catalytic and autocatalytic molecules unquestionably bear these two characteristics. For Dauvillier, "organic photosynthetic matter became living matter when oxidation metabolism began."[15] But that property is no less chemical than biological. Pascual Jordan affirms that "no more than we can establish exactly and objectively the precise boundary between the animal world and the vegetable world, can we trace a clear line of demarcation between the domains of organized beings and of molecules."[16] To conclude with Piveteau,

> in the beginning, living matter was hardly distinguishable from prime matter. A probable description might be droplets of protoplasm, the sites of reactions which physicochemistry could explain entirely but which contained within themselves, from the start, a mass of potentialities which would be realized gradually and progressively lead to the more highly organized forms.[17]

This progressive "complexification" of structures is the decisive characteristic of the ascent of order in the domain of life, as was the case in the atomic and molecular fields. At first, "the living environment must have been like . . . a bare protoplasm comprising innumerable nuclei. . . . The cell and its nucleus had not yet appeared."[18]

The tendency to individualization must have begun with this first tiny drop of protoplasm, a tendency which culminated in the emergence of cells, with or without membranes, and within these cells, chromatin, the vehicle

[14]*Naissance de la terre et de la vie sur la terre*, a publication of the International Center of Synthesis, p. 146.

[15] A. Dauvilliers, *Les Origines de la vie*, pp. 31–35.

[16] Jordan, op. cit., p. 74.

[17] *Naissance de la terre . . .* , p. 170.

[18] A. Dauvillier, op. cit., p. 146.

of hereditary properties, condensed to form a nucleus.[19]

Thus in the domain of living things one finds the same principle of individuation, or quantification, which, as we have already observed, dominates the world of inanimate beings. Little is known about the process that first associated macromolecules into organic units, next joined bacteria with nuclei that were not clearly defined, and then resulted in cells, bacteriophages, and complex particles that are perfectly individualized. But it is impossible not to be impressed by the parallel between the associative phenomenon which produces atoms and molecules and the process which results in bacteria and cells. The complexity of cellular structures inevitably calls to mind the similar process by which electrons irresistibly arrange themselves around the nucleus of an atom.

Although the exact nature of the interactions which led to the cell has not been determined, we can nevertheless observe with François Jacob that "a cell cannot be a mere collection of various types of molecule all closed up in a sack; it is in fact a society of molecules, whose members must all be kept 'informed' by a network of communications."[20]

It nevertheless seems certain that individuation among living things remained a simple process for many billions of years. During the entire Pre-Cambrian era, for instance, its only manifestation was bacteria, whose nuclei probably existed but were not clearly characterized, and blue-green algae. Piveteau concludes that for "three billion years vital action was almost exclusively geochemical, then biochemical, but it was by no means a matter of organic evolution."[21]

This geochemical action was an essential prerequisite for the development of life, because evolution could not have

---

[19] Piveteau, loc. cit.

[20] *Le Monde*, February 8, 1967.

[21] Unpublished lecture: "L'Apparition de la vie sur le globe dans la perspective de la paléontologie."

begun without a preliminary purifying of the earth's atmosphere. When the earth's crust was consolidated, there was no free oxygen, and therefore no ozone, in the atmosphere. And only a layer of ozone in the upper levels of the atmosphere could have screened out the ultraviolet rays of the sun, which are lethal. Without this protection, the only things that could develop were anaerobic marine bacteria, protected from the lethal rays by the sea. It was probably at this point that chlorophyll and its first effects were "invented."

The rays of the visible spectrum penetrate the sea to a depth of about 650 feet, whereas ultraviolet rays do not reach beyond about 15 inches. Because of the enormous proliferation of bacteria, the quantity of oxygen liberated by their chlorophyll was greater than the quantity they fixed. This free oxygen gradually spread through the atmosphere. Ultraviolet rays acted on this free oxygen to form ozone, which gradually created a screen above the earth's surface.

The first step in the history of life, then, occurred before the formation of the ozone screen, when life was possible within the sea only.

The second stage began when the ozone screen began to act as a shield. During the Pre-Cambrian era this stage was characterized in various areas by calcareous concretions of various forms analogous to those formed now by blue-green algae. These are very primitive organisms, like bacteria, but the work of Piekarski and Pascual Jordan,[22] has now shown with certainty that they have nuclei, each of which carries a chromosome.

Blue-green algae live in shallow waters but depend upon air. They could not develop until the earth's atmosphere was rich enough in oxygen and could not proliferate until the ozone screen was in existence.

Certain of these concretions—or, more exactly, the layers enclosing them—are at least 2½ billion years old. The ozone

---

[22] Jordan, op. cit., p. 139.

screen, therefore, is approximately as ancient, and it was under its protection that life began to develop.

A third phase began to open when, under the protection of the ozone screen, the atmosphere contained enough free oxygen for oxidation to become possible around the borderline between earth and water.

At that moment, about 500 million years ago, during the Cambrian era, the immense process of evolution was inaugurated with the spreading out and diversification of living matter. It began with the organization of the cell, a highly complex corpuscle enclosing within its individualizing membrane cytoplasm and a nucleus. The cytoplasm itself contains chondriosomes, or mitochondria, and Golgi bodies, which are apparently responsible for chemical change.

But the nucleus is the true command-post, the controlling center, of all cellular material. A delicate structure, its behavior in the process of reproduction is very complex.

Cells reproduce by amitosis or mitosis. Amitosis is a simple division into equal parts of the cytoplasm and the nucleus. In mitosis, filaments called chromosomes are formed within the nucleus; their number is characteristic of the species. Chromosomes split longitudinally, and their number doubles. Each group is then attracted to one of the two poles which have formed in the cytoplasmic mass, and, after a membrane which separates the two groups has formed, two cells identical to the first exist. The order which characterizes the first one has been faithfully reproduced.

The process is more complex in sexing cells. By a phenomenon known as chromatic reduction, male and female chromosomes—from the spermatozoon and the ovule respectively—pair off. Within the cell which will become the ovum, they form, by elimination of one of their number, chromosomes in equal number. These chromosomes come either from the father or from the mother.

Recent progress in genetics has made it possible to pinpoint chromosomes as the vehicles of hereditary characteristics. Each chromosome seems to be an accumulation of molecules of nucleic acid. Their extraordinary complexity allows for limitless variation, which explains the diversity of their individual characters.

It is not yet known how the quantum characteristics of a gene determine the macroscopic character of the individual an egg will produce. However, recent research, especially Pascual Jordan's work, has supported the argument that "a living cell acts like a magnifying device which permits an isolated microphysical action to have macrophysical repercussions. . . . That the cell is governed by microphysical elements has become a certainty."[23]

One of the major tasks currently facing biology now is to reveal the nature of the regulating devices involved in this governing mechanism. But there is already no doubt that they constitute the controlling phenomena that generates the immense doses of order with which the living substance is endowed.

Bacteria and other similar cells, having no chlorophyll, can acquire their nourishment directly from the mineral world. The deterioration of terrestrial minerals under their influence is observable as far back as the Archean era.

However, organic evolution very soon found itself at a major crossroad: in one direction lay the vegetable kingdom, which is provided with chlorophyll; in the other, the animal kingdom, which is not.

Chlorophyll is a catalytic molecule which produces a plant's constituent carbohydrates from carbonic gas and water vapor in the atmosphere, from nitrogen compounds in the soil, and from the photons in solar radiations.

Throughout the course of evolution, it was as if the vegetable kingdom was attempting to capture as much light energy as possible by means of its large leaves, through whose broad

[23] *Naissance de la terre . . .* , pp. 128ff., 136, 143.

surfaces chlorophyll works. At the same time that the efficiency of the machine increased, the number of photons absorbed for each molecule of carbonic gas rose, from one in some primitive plants to four in the most highly evolved species. When the sun is at its zenith, chlorophyll absorbs about two horsepower per square meter, which, over a period of one year at average latitudes, amounts to 0.1 horsepower per square meter.

The synthesis of carbohydrates is a process in which energy and matter are invested in the production of the extremely complex living substances known as vegetable matter. All the vegetation covering the face of the earth can therefore be considered a gigantic factory, producing order that has already reached a very high degree. But there is an absolute limit which cannot be exceeded by the energy-absorbing capabilities of an autotrophic living being nourished by the solar energy it has absorbed: this limit is the total amount of energy supplied by the sun to the outer surface of that being. An animal roughly the size of a man, if it were to depend only on solar radiation for its own energy, could expect to command no more than approximately 0.01 horsepower.[24] Its creative capacity would be far weaker than that of modern man, who requires more than ten times as much power to sustain his various activities.

At this stage of evolution a decisive advance took place. Instead of relying upon sun exposure to develop organic products by itself, the living being began to gather them from its immediate surroundings. These products were prepared either from already existing plants, in the case of herbivores or from other animals which depend upon plants in the case of carnivores. Heterotrophy appeared in both cases and decisively increased the amount of order life was able to generate.

[24] See A. Ducrocq, *Logique de la vie*. The ideas in the next several pages are drawn either verbatim or in a condensed form from this remarkable book. In fact, I owe more to its author than a few quotations: his analyses have stimulated my own ideas and have often guided me through my own reflections.

However, heterotrophy operates only when the cell in which it is vested can find near at hand the other cells that are to be its victims. Hence evolution attempted another solution: fungi, which, being entirely without chlorophyll, draw their sustenance from the organic medium on which they settle. In this instance the formula worked very well: today 40,000 types of fungi are known, some of them very highly evolved; the myomycetes, for example, like amoebas, eat the germs they encounter. The possibilities for fungi were nevertheless limited. Condemned to parasitic life, they could only organize whatever desirable substances and energy they found in the environment that provided their nourishment.

In order to increase its ordering powers, a living being must not limit itself to passive encounters with any kind of food. It must search for the type of food suited to it, wherever it is likely to be found. At first mobility in an isolated cell was simply the outcome of a mere change of form. In protista, for example, motion does not seem to be oriented; simply by widening the area the cell can explore, it increases the cell's chances of encountering a prey. Only much later, with the development of feelers and other sensoria—primitive forms of eventual nervous systems—is the animal able to carry out movements oriented toward goals that are more and more precisely defined.

The beginning of movement was also the beginning of a high adventure: kinetic autonomy. It transformed the animal into an increasingly powerful creator and exalter of order.

The first two techniques to be perfected during this extraordinary development were grasping and moving about. Grasping food was soon to be guaranteed by a specialized orifice, the mouth, which would eventually be equipped with accessories adapted to its needs, though for a long time it retained its characteristic form of a long snout. The situation did not change until much later, when the assumption of an upright posture freed two limbs of any locomotor function, so that they could be specialized for grasping activity. Then, instead of grasping its food with its mouth, the animal began to take it in its hands. After that, the mouth no longer served for collecting food, and the face could lose the length characteristic of animals.[25]

The consequences of this mutation will be mentioned in the discussion of the evolution of the head, a major characteristic of the human structure.

The ability to move from one place to another also led to significant advances. At first the technique was rudimentary, and the results poor. Some animals depended upon propulsion by reaction (as is still the case with the jellyfish), or flagella, which certain cells have. Eventually the amoeba's pseudopods—an important step in the technique of moving about—appeared.

Because of its fins, the fish was granted a more rational solution, and one which was to have profound repercussions. In fact, two alternatives were available, and both were tried. The first was a large fin with a wide base as a line of articulation for many parallel ribs; this efficient solution made possible movement from one place to another at great speed. The second, which implied remarkable consequences, consisted of lobed fins. Much sturdier than the single fin, they enabled the species that developed them to move about in marshy terrain.

When certain seas dried up, during the period when geological evidence indicates some landmasses shifted, the only species that survived were those equipped anatomically to gain a footing on land or in coastal marshes. Hence we can project the appearance and spread of amphibians through natural

---

[25] Ibid., p. 191.

selection. "Thus life set out to conquer the continents, giving birth first to reptiles and then to mammals."[26]

Numerous differences among the species began to appear. Although they seem to have been logically coordinated, it may be that their coherence is the result of natural selection. The only species to have lived and survived are those equipped with suitable means to ensure and defend their existence. Thus certain herbivores, freed from the need to find nourishment by attacking other living beings, were gradually equipped with limbs better suited to running, which enabled them to escape their predators. Carnivorous animals, on the other hand, were to be equipped for combat.

The extremely improbable coexistence of vegetable and animal life resulted in a regulatory phenomenon which is highly characteristic of those mechanisms that confer endurance. It seems inevitable, at first glance, that animal life should have dominated vegetable life. Plants are defenseless before animals, which can see them from afar and move toward them to devour them. As it eats the plant, however, the animal reduces the energy sources necessary to maintain its ability to move. As a result of this kind of trade-off, there arose in every area, through spontaneous regulation, an appropriate balance between the respective densities of the vegetable and the animal settlements.

In each of the two kingdoms, vegetable and animal, life was offered another choice. It might, theoretically at least, switch over to the formula of the asocial cell, which formed protophytic or protozoic populations, or to that of the cell associating with its fellows to form metazoa.

Protista tended toward the perfection of their organization. Some developed the technique of movement through succes-

26 Ibid., pp. 192–193.

sive deformations; others chose to seek and devour their prey through a set of highly developed muscular fibrilla:

> Paramecia carried originality to the point of bearing the trichocysts, which snap off, just like arrows capable of wounding an attacking enemy. Similarly, stentors reaching a lighted area begin a recoiling operation, then pivot around on their hind part, and move away in another direction. Jennings, the physiologist, studied these behaviors and considered it possible to speak of a certain type of genuine psychism at the level of the cell.[27]

Compared to metazoa, however, protista were ultimately in an inferior position. Like Robinson Crusoe on his island, they had to perform a great variety of functions and, therefore, could carry out each of them in only an amateur fashion. The metazoon, on the other hand, was able to specialize its organs and perfect their various functions, though its evolution was slower because of the greater diversity of the solutions it had to investigate.

The metazoon's trials and errors affected both its form and functioning. At first it was nearly spherical, with a mouth and an anus. The dimensions of the cellular society it constituted grew with the number of members, and its form elongated in the same direction as its movement. But a mechanical problem soon arose: the rigidity of the whole. So long as the living being consisted of a small collection of cells, those cells remained closely linked as a result of their mutual interactions. But this link-to-link assemblage became inadequate as soon as the animal reached such considerable size that its form was at the mercy of external forces.

If a complex organic society was to be rigid, two solutions were available. Either the entire ensemble of associated cells could be enclosed in a solid shell, like a box, or the whole

[27] Ibid., pp. 197ff.

group could be mounted on a solid chassis. The first solution is the carapace, the second the skeleton. Because of the guarantees they afforded, both solutions represented a decisive advance. The former yielded the invertebrates, the latter the vertebrates. The invertebrates were to include, mainly, the crustaceans and the arthropods; later, those crustaceans that had become airborne were to be called insects.

At first the vertebrates' renunciation of the protection of a carapace was an unhappy choice. It left them exposed to the challenges of the external world. Gradually, however, by resisting the various forms these challenges took, they achieved their greatest advances. Most of the dangers threatening an organism arise from the accidents to which it is exposed, and those accidents are themselves the random results of encounters between independent causal series. By establishing within its very body an "internal medium" protected from the risks of the outer world by the most subtle mechanism, the organism gains a relatively stable ambience. The margins of uncertainty it has to face are reduced, and its autonomy, and hence the liberty whose vehicle it becomes, is increased.

The emergence of this landlocked sea, as it were, implied first of all a change in form. The development moved from a ball of cells, like the volvox, to a tea-cosy shape, like that of certain sponges. The human embryo recapitulates this evolution as it passes from the morula to the blastula stage.

The true internal medium eventually appeared as the coelenterata. This consisted of a mass of water enclosed within a cavity, access to which was through a mouth. The animal constantly renews this reserve of water by selectively drawing upon the vast resources of the ocean in which it swims. This evolutionary process culminated in the emergence of blood, a liquid salty like the water of the sea of which, according to Quinton, it is vaguely reminiscent.

But the landlocked sea could sustain only riparian cells. To increase the number of cells and, with it, the complexity of the organism, the ambient water had to reach every part of the animal. This was achieved by the appearance of a system of distribution in the form of a network of blood vessels.

The circulation of blood in a closed circuit, however, poses two essential problems. A continuing feeding process is required to ensure that the composition of the blood remains constant, despite unforeseeable fluctuations in external events. Moreover, the blood must rotate regularly between the sites where consumption occurs and those where nourishment takes place. Nourishment involves both a supply of combustibles and a combustor: the former may be solid or liquid, the latter is always a gas, oxygen. In view of the differences in their consistencies, it is obvious that the two elements of nourishment could not be drawn from the external world by the same process. Two systems—the respiratory and the digestive—were evolved and specialized; the first collects oxygen through the nostrils, the second ingests food through the muzzle or mouth. The transfer of oxygen was effected by specialized cells, the red blood corpuscles, which function as oxygen carriers by fixing the nourishing gas with the iron they contain.

It was still necessary, however, that the "landlocked sea" be protected against external hazards and the accidental intrusion of undesirable elements. Leucocytes, with their bacteria-destroying ability, were to perform this passive defense function.

Finally, in order that the blood might reach every part of the organism, an accelerator was required. This was the heart, a true lift-and-force pump. Its development was the outcome of a gradual transformation of a simple contractile vessel like the one still found in the heart of the coelacanth.

The supreme refinement of the internal network in mammals was effected with the regulation of bodyheat. While reptiles were left utterly defenseless against the many hazards of climatic variations—which was to bring about, eventually, their almost complete extinction—warmblooded animals enjoyed an almost constant internal temperature.

The circulatory system is a communication network equipped to transmit from one organ to another certain information-bearing substances, the hormones. These are the genuine messengers of physiological regulation.

This method of signal communication was slow and crude to develop, however. During the progressive evolution of species, it was soon duplicated by courier service performed by another specialized system. In fact, the nervous system stands in relation to the hormonal system as modern telegraph networks do to transmission by pneumatic tube. The information-collecting organs that make up the five senses form a system together with the transmission complex of the neurons. To these elements are added certain centralizing and refining faculties which perform data-processing functions. These determine the messages that are sent to the "effectuators," such as the muscles. The latter carry out the gestures, and therefore the acts, which are the basis of behavior.

Throughout this development, the brain played a most important role as the center for collecting and sorting data. Its size and weight, relative to the size and weight of any other animal, apparently increase in proportion to the degree of its psychic activity. The coelacanth's brain, for instance, represents only about 15/1,000 of its body weight, while man's brain is about 1/50.

Obviously, such rough correlations between the brain's relative weight and the degree of mental activity cannot be regarded as a measure of intelligence. They do, nevertheless, indicate a certain direction in evolution, one which is of capital importance to the progress of species. They also make it easier to assess the complexity of the cerebral apparatus, which must be measured in terms of a number of neurons infinitely greater than the number of connections in even the most sophisticated electronic machines.

However important the gradual complexification of the brain and its correlation with the development the psychical faculties may be, even the effects of brain disorders on behavior reveal nothing about that mysterious presence which is the "person" of the thinking being. Although undoubtedly linked to the brain, it is as different from it as a computer programmer is from the hardware or the software he uses.

The emergence of the human person among the hominids effected a genuine mutation in the machinery through which order in the universe has been steadily growing in quantity and quality. The third part of this book will deal with the characteristics and the consequences of this mutation. But before taking up that topic, we must examine the enormous amount of order brought into the universe by animal groups.

The level of animal societies

Although an animal is a complex society of specialized organs, it is unquestionably an individual. However, this individual may be social or asocial, as is true at every level of organization. If it is asocial, i.e. if it has no perceptible interaction with its fellows, the animal will pursue a solitary life; if, on the other hand, it is social, i.e. if it is the agent and object of interactions, it will join with its fellows to form more or less coordinated groups. Those groups, in turn, will form, on the next higher plane, a new organizational level: the level of animal societies.

Animal societies are far more than the charming fantasy of amateur naturalists. On the contrary, under the brilliant leadership of Professor Grassé, the study of animal sociology has been one of the most fruitful and active branches of zoology in France.

Almost every species is social to some degree. For example, termitaries, the long strings of processionary caterpillars, the nests of republican grosbeaks, and beaver villages are all instances of animal societies. So are swarms of locusts, herds of deer, seal harems, clans of monkeys, certain groups of spiders, and migrating flights of *Danais archippus* butterflies.

Marcel Sire has provided an impressive inventory and classification of the various types of animal society.

Animal societies may be temporary or permanent. When temporary, they are often based on sexual phenomena or reproduction requirements. They give rise to gestures which seem to express affection or love—those, for instance, between a cock and a hen pigeon or on the part of a mother protecting her little ones.

Philosophers have long speculated about the similarities between individuals and animal societies. The analysis of such analogies by Herbert Spencer is now of historic interest only, of course. Nevertheless, it did herald the ideas of modern biologists, who see a parallel between certain animal societies and such highly integrated invertebrate organisms as sponges. A beehive, for example, has as many holes as a sponge and is the site of an intense circulation of air, just as a sponge is the site of a great circulation of seawater. In a hive the nutrients move from one individual to another, in a sponge, from one cell to another. A hive comprises both male and female individuals, so it can rightly be called hermaphroditic; a sponge is also hermaphroditic, but at the cellular level. More generally:

> The differentiated cells of the soma or body of a living being correspond to the neuters of animal societies. Like them, they function for the good of the entire organism, sacrificing themselves so that it can live. Germinal or reproductive cells in animals are represented in animal societies by the royal animals; like them, they live off the activity of the neuters. Similarly they are immortal in the sense that they recreate themselves in their progeny.[28]

[28] E. L. Bouvier, quoted by M. Sire, *La Vie sociale des animaux*, p. 184.

Division of labor, which is related to the morphological differentiation of castes, includes the intervention of social hormones and the socialization of food.

In genuine insect societies, because of the automatic coordination of activity, order prevails in the absence of government to enforce it. "A society of vertebrates lives within a territory organized under the control of a more or less stable hierarchy, which often neutralizes natural aggressiveness and disciplines tendencies and, as a result, activities as well."[29] Every higher animal society has a language, a system of signs which make communication possible. These signs may be tactile (the stroking of antennae), olfactory (urine may have an important, but not exclusive, function here), or gesticulatory (the dance of bees). Communication is established by means of specialized senses, which in every case play the same role as the "effectuata" in cybernetics.

Many species live within the context of a strict social hierarchy (ducks, farmyard chickens, fish in an aquarium, birds in linear or triangular formation). Finally, almost every social species evidences a sense of ownership, vigorously defending its territory or living space against intruding rival species (fish, frogs and lizards, birds, mammals). A living space or territory is genuinely organized into clearly defined zones (a hare's seat and secondary forms; a beaver's burrows with their escape exits, airshafts, rest-rooms and sleeping chambers, storerooms, bridal chamber, dams, watering places, pastures, hunting grounds, playgrounds and sunny terraces).

The haunts are connected by tracks which become genuine paths when they have been used by a number of successive generations. As far as elephants are concerned, they may be three to five yards wide, stripped

[29] Ibid., p. 187.

clean of all vegetation. American bisons in their migrations cleared real roads which were frequently used by man as railroad beds. All along these paths animals place road-signs: a pile of dung, urine, peeled treetrunks, secretions from one gland or another, etc. They make it easier for them to find their way, which is so important in times of danger, when a refuge must be reached promptly.[30]

Thus, all animal societies, different and various though they may seem, are organized "wholes." And, like all societies, they "are" and they "do."

To the extent that they "are," such societies encompass within lasting structures individual behaviors. Thus they generate real quanta of existence which may include a great number of individuals (termitaries, for instance). But their existence brings about the emergence of new abilities. It is because they possess these abilities that animal societies appear suited to certain tasks: the protection, nourishment, and raising of progeny; the establishment and defense of a territory; investment in food reserves; resistance to the hazards of existence. Like true machines, animal societies create an order which is more complex than the one which their members embodied. They are a significant stage in the continuing progress of social order throughout the universe.

[30] Ibid., pp. 180–181.

PART III

Prometheus

Prometheus, one of the Titans, is responsible for a major turning-point in the evolution of the universe. It was he, according to Hesiod, who created men and gave them heaven's fire. Initially the secularization of fire was an extremely trivial occurrence. After a sordid argument about dividing a sacrificed bullock, Jupiter, says Hesiod in his Theogony, *withheld inextinguishable fire from suffering mankind. But Iapetus's noble son, Prometheus, clever enough to trick the ruler of Olympus, stole a spark and hid it. Jupiter who thunders in the heavens was deeply hurt when he saw the protracted glow of the flame in the midst of men, and his anger flared up.*

The possession of the secret of fire by beings endowed with human characteristics profoundly altered the process of the creation of order in the universe. The immense islands of existence on which newly created men were to settle had emerged without human intervention of any sort. They simply "were," and we have no certain knowledge of how and why they came into existence.

Henceforth, increasingly complex and far-reaching orders were to come into existence. We know that, unlike their predecessors, these new orders were created by men and that their "creators" deliberately brought them into existence because they desired—for themselves or for others—the benefits that an ordered state, which they had chosen from among all those possible, could provide. Order, whose finality had, until then, been mysterious, now became the fulfillment of human volitions. It was easy to locate, and its nature, goal, and means were known from man's immediate awareness of his creative power.

Here we shall address ourselves to the consequences of this Promethean revolution.

CHAPTER VI

The Promethean Mutation

By THE TIME of the "Prometheus incident," a creation had already accumulated quantities of order, first in inanimate nature and then in the realm of life. These had achieved a high degree of complexity with the advent of the most recent innovations, vertebrates and insects. One might have speculated that all the order potentially contained in the fundamental particles had now materialized, that all the possibilities of creation had been exhausted. But with this twofold initiative—the creation of men and the theft of fire—Prometheus opened up a new chapter in the epic of order.

Toward the end of the Tertiary period, his first action conferred three major features on a group of mammals that had hitherto been barely differentiated:

Because they had become able to walk upright, their hands were freed of any ambulatory function. Thus they were rendered suitable for the refined gestures which were to bring on *homo faber*.

Because they were now vertical bipeds, their skulls took a position in the skeleton which allowed them to increase in size. Thus it was possible for the brain to develop in volume and complexity.

Because they could now use their hands to convey food to their mouths, their mouths were free to develop away from a muzzle form. This opened the way for the structuration of the breathing apparatus and the upper digestive tract into forms which allowed the transition from rudimentary sounds emitted by higher animals to the sophisticated modulation of articulate language.[1]

The theft of fire, the second Promethean initiative, provided the beneficiaries with enormous stores of energy. Consequently, it offered virtually unlimited increase of their power. A brain controlling a hand, governing vocal cords, and exercising full power over reserves of energy previously accumulated—such was the animal which, during the evolutionary progress of the universe, was to accomplish the far-reaching Promethean revolution.

Because of its other characteristics, however, this being remained a vertebrate mammal. That is, it was an infinitely complex machine which converted matter and energy into its own substance and protected its place in the universe through reproduction and the use of those offensive and defensive means that Nature had put at its disposal. The new equipment which characterized the Promethean revolution did not constitute a break in animal evolution so much as a refinement of existing devices: the brain, the fingers, the gullet. All of these had existed earlier in higher species, especially the primates. But while the improvement of these organs was simply a further extension of an evolution that had extended over thousands of years, its consequences were to bring about a radical change in the behavior of the beings it affected.

[1] See Dr. Chauchard, *Sociétés humaines*, p. 94.

Promethean psychism

The Promethean biped does not monopolize psychism. Wherever there is "existence," there is also behavior. That is, in response to signals received from the outer world, a unique path emerges, mapped out within the narrow channel of the possible.

The concept of behavior is familiar to anyone who observes living beings. Until recent years, however, it was considered irrelevant to inanimate objects: they, in their passivity, were endowed with "being," but not with "existence."

Since Heisenberg's discovery of the uncertainty principle, however, particulate indeterminism has been universally accepted—subject to the scrupulous doubts entertained by Louis de Broglie in his latest book (see the Postscript to Chapter 2). This implies the functioning of a mechanism capable of extracting the present from the whole range of the possibles. In fact we know nothing of the nature of such a mechanism. But we are fully aware that even among inanimate beings individual behavior—that of radioactive molecules, for instance—is a burst of spontaneity. As such, it must be distinguished from the strict determinism observed in populations comprising a great number of individuals.

There is of course no need to stress that, contrary to appearances, particulate indeterminism is simply one of the most elementary requirements of common sense. In fact, if a particle's path were entirely determined, the history of the world, even in its most remote developments, would also be determined. According to Laplace, whose views are well known and whom we have already quoted,

> an intelligence which, at any given moment, could know all the forces animating Nature and the respective positions of all the beings of which it is composed—provided, of course, that it was of such an all-embracing nature

that it could analyze all these data—would in a single formula encompass the motions of the largest bodies in the universe and those of the smallest atom; nothing would be uncertain to it, and the future as well as the past would unfold before its eyes.

But we know from unquestionable experience that the history of the world is not determined, that the thoughts and actions of certain individuals can affect its course.

Particulate indeterminism is not the unanticipated result of some abstruse theory, but the door through which freedom came into the world. Observation of behavior reveals that it is present everywhere, notwithstanding the strict determinism apparent in macroscopic phenomena. The latter are the outcome of the law of large numbers.

Although mathematics may have needed such indeterminism to explain the concrete appearances of the world of particles, it is in the realm of life, even of the most elemental type, that the concept of individual behavior has blossomed forth. The light-seeking tree, the amoeba that covets its prey, the spermatozoon rushing toward the ovum, the hen pecking at grain—none of these merely "is": they "behave," inasmuch as they have a certain way of being in the world, a specific mode of existence in relation to the surrounding universe from which they receive signals. In each case, it seems as though the living being "willed" the advantages its behavior will bring it and acts with a view to achieving them.

On the other hand, all subhuman activities demonstrate a common characteristic, albeit in varying degrees. Notwithstanding their margin of indeterminism, they depend exclusively on the means with which Nature has endowed the actors. No matter how subtle the action, it is initiated by a signal that accords with a pre-set program. This recalls those taped programs that control automated machines: there is no distinction between ends and means. In this respect, nothing is more typical than the bird's continual accumulation of food in its nest, for itself and its young, even after the bottom of the nest has been knocked out. Similarly a cat, after relieving itself, will conscientiously scratch away at its tray even when there is no sand in it. An animal does not act in a specific way because it desires the end the action will achieve or because the action is an efficient means of attaining that end, but because it follows a program of automatic responses cybernetically stored, so to speak, in its biological inheritance.

Those responses that are common to all members of the same species are automatic, innate, perfect from the outset, and unchangeable. The fact that they are, of course, oriented toward a definite goal may lend them the appearance of rationality, but the two examples just cited demonstrate that whatever rationality is present is not in the agent but in the creative process that is responsible for the linkages that determine the action. Similar behavior patterns can be found among all living species, whether vegetable or animal, and also in certain human organs—the stomach, the heart, the lungs—that carry out the vegetative functions of the human species. In all of these cases, the act seems one indivisible whole: it is triggered in its entirety by a signal; there is virtually no faculty of adaptation. The end is never distingued from the means.

The rift between ends and means

The higher on the ladder of species, however, the more obvious the difference between a desired end and the means suitable for achieving it. On the lower levels there is hardly any difference. Piéron mentions the case of limpets which encrust sea rocks but move about to feed on algae. They always return to exactly the same spots, where the texture of the rock precisely matches the texture of their shells. If one of the resting places is destroyed during its absence, the returning limpet will not stop there but will hesitate and explore the area with its tentacles, showing that it recalls its starting point and its direction away and homeward.

Piéron also describes an experiment with species of ants which return to their nests carrying grain collected during their journey. He managed to get one of the ants onto a blade of grass and, by way of deception, moved it some distance away. The ant resumed its progress and, when it had traveled the same distance it would have needed to reach the nest, it became agitated, excitedly reconnoitering the territory in search of the nest. It had retained an extremely precise kinesthetic memory of the distance it had traveled.[2]

Certain dogs demonstrate rudiments of rational behavior: deprived of food and shut in a room with several exits, some of which are closed, they will search for the exit that will take them to the desired food. Some monkeys seem to differentiate between a desired end and the means of attaining it:

> They use stones against their enemy, and take up anything with which they can hit. Hunters know that it is possible to get coconuts easily by throwing stones at monkeys in coconut trees: the monkeys use the coconuts to throw back at the people who have thrown stones at them. A nut used like this is certainly a tool. . . . Similarly, gorillas and chimpanzees will use wooden clubs and tree-limbs.[3]

Only in man, however, is the distinction between end and means so clear and conscious that the desire to obtain the former stimulates a thorough search for the latter. This dissociation implies an idea—that is, a clear and distinct representation or notion of the objective to be attained.

But every idea is derived from a rift in our various states of consciousness. Water cannot be drawn from a river without

[2] Henri Piéron, "De l'Animal à l'homme," in *A la Recherche de la mentalité préhistorique*, 1950, pp. 45–47.

[3] Ibid., pp. 52–53.

a container of some sort. Similarly, an idea cannot be extracted from the stream of consciousness unless it is enclosed in a word; this ensures its transferability but, at the same time, divests it of its relationships with allied thoughts. A clear and distinct idea is therefore the product of articulate speech and remains beyond the capabilities of animals that can only low, mew, or bark. Therefore a clear and distinct idea is linked to verbalized thinking and is a Promethean privilege; it implies and demands adequate adjustment of the throat and enough cerebral development to control the vocal cords.

The use of words to represent ideas introduces into the life of the mind a fundamental quantification, analogous to that effected by the condensation of energy into particles of matter. As soon as such quantification occurred, the goal of a gesture was no longer inevitably associated, in the consciousness of the being which made it, with the means leading to it or with the signal that caused it to be desired. It was now possible to distinguish each step in the causal series leading to the act and to consider each of them separately. Thus, in the whole chain of indistinct reactions which gradually lead the animal from feeling hunger to the pursuit of prey, man consciously distinguishes cause, i.e. the need for nourishment, from the means of satisfying it, which prompt him to search for or prepare food, and from the satisfaction he derives from eating it.

This splitting of the stream of consciousness into particles of verbalized thought generated a fundamental modification in the psychism that gives rise to behavior. Before the emergence of verbalized thought, the causal series extending from the sensory signal to the act was a closed circuit: each stage inevitably led to the next, and none of them could be separated or isolated. After the advent of verbalized thought, the end, and the end alone, became the desired goal. The signal no longer triggers off an act, but an aspiration, a desire, or a volition.

When a modern man is cold, he wishes that a heating system

were present in the place where he lives. But he does not automatically light a fire. Searching for the best way of getting warm, he may use wood, coal, or oil, depending on the situation in which he finds himself.

Thus, for man, who is capable of verbalized thought, the stream of thought that leads from feeling cold to the best way of getting warm is exposed. The gap between the signal which originates it and the satisfaction which terminates it can be filled in by the means best suited to achieve the desired end. It is through this gap that tools are introduced into the causal series of efficient action.

Animals are the media for action; man is the medium for ends.

The computer of emergence

Liberated from biological automatism in the voluntary and conscious aspects of his behavior but impelled by the pursuit of certain goals, the Promethean creature recognized that he was obliged to seek out the best means of attaining them.

He succeeded by using those faculties that distinguish him most from all other beings:

> The specificity of man does not lie in social life, not even in language as a signal or a medium for communication, but in the use of language not to talk *to* . . . but to talk *about*. Thus, man has produced works of the mind that can be accumulated, transmitted, and reinterpreted. . . . He does not stop at seeing, he reads; he deciphers all forms and, behind the forms, their meaning, which he assimilates into himself.[4] What is fundamentally singular about man is that he can transmit new ideas, an ability which is found nowhere else in the animal kingdom.[5]

[4] Raymond Ruyer, *L'Animal, l'homme*, 1964, p. 261.
[5] Jacques Monod, in an interview published in *Le Monde*, December 9, 1965.

By devising the word or the symbol as a medium of expression, articulated language imparted new precision and wider application to memory and imagination. Above all, it made possible the use of a powerful machine, the machine of reason. Taking advantage of the economy of thought resulting from the substitution of a word for the meaning ascribed to it, man was able to use his deductive power to extract at any time from all the information used in his arguments the meanings they encompassed. "All men are mortal; John is a man; therefore John is mortal." If the two minor terms are true, the major certainly is, because it is nothing more than a particular expression of the general affirmations contained in the premises.

Formal logic is a "machine" because it automatically performs, and with a high rate of efficiency, the processing of the data conveyed by the minor terms. But formal logic is really nothing more than a systematization of ordinary thought processes. Even higher animals seem to make use of it, insofar as they can be trained or conditioned.

I do not propose to dwell at great length on the origin of human rationality: is it a gift of God or a fortuitous inherent characteristic? Or does it operate by analogy, reproducing the linkages among perceptible phenomena on the scale on which man observed them when they first emerged, i.e. prior to the invention of the electron microscope? I leave it to others to decide these serious questions, if they can.

It is remarkable, however, that the need for rational explanation is so widespread that it generated the fundamental religiosity universally characteristic of the human species. Unable to know the cause of the great natural phenomena, haunted by the mystery of death, and deeply and intensely convinced that sacrifice and prayer could influence the course of events in the world which surrounded them, men invented the gods: Jupiter, Neptune, Saturn and, before them, the whole pantheon of animistic myths. For men hungry for explanations, these divinities were the "sufficient reasons" for their universe.

They were the causes of perceptible phenomena, because they had been created to account for them.

The constant exercise of reasoning, its role, and its efficacy caused philosophers to focus their attention on the nature of the deductive process. Aristotle, for one, was led by his study of it to codify in his *Organon* the rules of formal logic, i.e. "of that part of logic which lays down rules for reasoning regardless of the content of the thought to which the reasoning process applies."[6] These and similar studies brought to a high degree of perfection the mechanics of syllogism, a formula that demonstrates that, once certain things are posited, other things necessarily follow from the mere fact that the first were posited.[7]

Syllogistic logic is a genuine thought-controlling system, a "machine" that establishes a necessary input/output relationship.

Awareness of the possibilities opened up by the syllogistic method created such enthusiasm that for two thousand years logic was the object of the meditations and intellectual exercises of all philosophers. What is most typical of such meditations and exercises is the *a priori* nature of the meanings attached to the symbols or propositions used. Whether the discussion was of gods or essences, quiddities or hidden causes, the premises and symbols originated in the minds of men. Rarely were they inherent in the nature of things.

At the beginning of the seventeenth century Sir Francis Bacon inaugurated the great revolution which gave birth to experimental science and which culminated in the most recent phases of modern scientific theory. Its bases—axioms, principles, postulates, definitions—no longer claim to express the essence of a concrete reality which they tend to ignore. Instead,

[6] Emile Bréhier, *Histoire de la Philosophie*, Vol. I, 1, p. 172.
[7] Aristotle, *First Analytics*, I, 1 (24 b 18).

the bases serve as mere points of departure for reasoning which will lead deductively to the propositions that have been recognized as the expression of perceptible phenomena. For these bases, the criterion of truth is not a coincidence with the essence of "things," which in any case we do not know, but only the explanatory force which attaches to them. Thus, day after day, theoretical science increasingly appears to be a "creation of causes."[8]

What is striking is that such causes make it possible not only to explain known facts, which is their function, but also to predict, within a certain surrounding area, relations hitherto unknown. This is not, however, an absolute possibility. The "causes" are always subject to revision, but so long as they remain efficient for prediction, they are the source of the power of modern science.

Causes that have been confirmed by experience enable man to deduct what he does not yet know from what he already knows. Thus he can predict effects that will "emerge" from new situations he himself may bring about. Electronic computing methods have augmented this predictive faculty by enormously increasing the number of factors that can be considered at one time in order to foresee an event or a phenomenon or to analyze a complex set of circumstances. These methods have made possible the new disciplines of operational research.

At this point man's ability to predict is virtually unlimited. He can prognosticate with greater and greater accuracy, and to an increasing extent, the capabilities of the tools or combinations of tools—in other words, the machines—he has the power to invent. This ability has made him a genuine "computer of emergence."

[8] This was the fundamental contention of my first book, *Des Sciences physiques aux sciences morales*, 1921, translated into English in 1929 and published by the Johns Hopkins University Press and Oxford University Press; revised edition in French, 1969.

The machine builder

In order to enjoy the benefits of a tool or a machine—a purposeful combination of tools—it is not enough merely to imagine them; ultimately, they must also be realized.

In this respect, the history of chipped flint, the mother of the first family of tools invented by man, teaches us a decisive lesson. For thirty years now, thanks to experimental technology, we have known exactly what gestures produced the various successive forms of cutting stones. To make a "nucleus," one strikes the flint perpendicularly to its surface. Such a blow breaks off a smooth, oblique flake, the initial form of a cutting tool, which is called a Clactonian flake. Three types of tools can be made from the Clactonian flake by striking it:

"choppers," flakes taken from one of the edges and with
   a crude cutting edge
double-edged flakes
pyramidal tools, made by chipping at both edges

"The most primitive forms of technical activity we know of is the production of Clactonian flakes, dihedral flakes, choppers, and pyramidal tools."[9]

All these tools were obtained by controlling human energy through the subtle gestures made possible by the hand. The hand thus appears as a natural tool which generated other tools, just as machines make other machines in a machine tool factory. The same process underlies the manufacture of those complicated tools which are combined to make machines. They are all the direct or indirect products of human energy controlled by the subtle tool, the hand, whose presence as part of man's body Prometheus made possible. The combination in man of the ability to imagine and the capacity to produce

[9] Leroi-Gourhan, in *A la Recherche* . . . , p. 81.

created the "machine builder" who is the real hero of the
Promethean epic.

Breaking into the energy resources of the universe

The essential purpose of a machine is to convert energy so
that the person using it can fulfill his aim. When the machine
is hand-operated, it uses only human energy. Such is the
case when man uses a double-edged flake, a knife, a lever,
or a winch.

A machine, however, does nothing more than restore the
energy that is put into it. At best, as in the case of a winch,
it can accumulate potential energy by lifting weights that will
eventually return the energy received.

But the strength of a man nourished only by the sunlight
received on his outer surface would not exceed 0.01 horsepower. His capacity for action has been greatly enhanced
by heterotrophy, a "device" which gives him the privilege
of feeding on the enriched energy contained in animal foods.
Such foods themselves are the outcome of a transformation
effected by the animals of autotrophic plants, which, through
photosynthesis, are able to feed directly on solar radiation.

Yet, even though man had at his disposal the vast factory
provided by the leaves of trees, his strength might have
remained limited by the amount of enriched energy the human
organism could digest during one time unit. The Promethean
revolution, which was inaugurated by the conquest of fire,
led man to break into the enormous reserves of solar energy
accumulated through the course of time in wood, in fossilized
plants, which became coal and oil, in the water lifted by evapo-
ration and stored in mountain reservoirs, in molecules (through
the use of chemical explosives, like gunpowder), and,
ultimately, in the nucleus of the atom.

Almost without effort, and by means of monitoring control

systems, man himself controls the valves that regulate the flow of the energy he has brought under his power. Each day, then, renews Prometheus's theft from the Creator of His instrument of power. But thanks to man's breaking into ever richer stores of energy, the daily theft of fire increases indefinitely—today, one can say almost boundlessly—the creative power of the human intellect.

Dei Adjutores [10]

Henceforth Prometheus's sons, with the hands their wills control and by means of the energy reserves over which their technology has given them free disposition, have the ability to achieve whatever their intellect conceives in the vast field of the possibles. They have become genuine "creators."

They have no more freedom of creative action than Jupiter, however. They make use of the interactions operating between particles at the various levels of organization; they cannot create new ones. In general, they simply intensify existing interactions by bringing closer together the individuals from which they emanate and by providing the energy necessary for the construction of a new society. By bringing an electron and a proton closer together, for example, and by increasing their respective speeds, a physicist makes or modifies an atom; by mixing in a crucible the elements he wishes to combine and by creating energy relations a chemist constantly re-creates the whole world before us.

However, the mechanics of human creation remain quite different from those of Nature—if not in principle, at least in their modalities. Man usually utilizes solids, and especially steel, while Nature more frequently uses gases or liquids. Man tends to rely on mechanical transformation, Nature on

[10] *Dei enim sumus adjutores* (We are laborers together with God), St. Paul, First Epistle to the Corinthians, III:9.

physical or chemical reactions. Finally, human production is generally effected at high temperatures and with methods that lack the subtlety of those which produce living beings. Nevertheless, the physics of plastics is currently progressing in its imitation of Nature. Day by day, the evolution of arts and techniques seems to be bringing us closer and closer to vital reactions.

Consequently, the major, if not the only, difference between Promethean and Jupiterian creation lies in the fact that in the former mode we are aware of the thought that conceives, of the will that decides, and of the hand that accomplishes, whereas in the latter the motive and, almost always, the means, escape us.

On the other hand, both creative processes converge in the same result: the passage of a being from a potential to an actual state, which means conferring existence.

In the words of the Apostle, "We are laborers together with God."

CHAPTER VII

The Actors in the Promethean Epic

Endowed with creative power and acting as laborers together with God, the children of Prometheus assumed vast responsibilities for determining the structures of their universe. But, as social animals par excellence, they generated, at levels above themselves, a series of societies in which all, or at least some, of their faculties were vested. Men and the societies formed by them have actuated and controlled the Promethean evolution of the world in which they settled.

Private individuals are the fundamental particles in human societies

The human person is the fundamental particle in societies of men. Like any one of the particles composing lower organizations, it is indivisible: division destroys it. Nor is there any need to define it: each of us has immediate knowledge of the person he is because he is conscious of the continuity of his existence, despite the accidents and changes which may affect it between birth and death.

A human person always has a living organism as its medium,

however, and it may be difficult to distinguish one from the other. This feature is what transforms it into a particle.

At the same time, however, it, like all fundamental particles, is the subject and the object of remote actions. Such actions take place between the human person and inanimate objects or living beings, in particular other human persons. No one, for example, would deny that the sexual attraction between a man and woman or the feeling uniting a married couple with their offspring is interaction. Such relationships are wavelike in nature. They enable us to see in the human person the wave-corpuscle complementarity which characterizes all fundamental particles.

The interactions to which a person is subject determine his behavior. We have noted already that behavior is a response of the person to the messages transmitted to him by the outside world—a response which, when conscious, tends to provide the satisfaction which the person considers most desirable and which can be obtained through the least undesirable efforts. Thus human behavior is an unending quest for maximum desirability. But the results of all possible acts are appraised by those who could accomplish them in relation to their own scale of values. It is because he is what he is that a normal man responds to the appeal of a woman, or a normal mother to the love of her child.

It is difficult, if not impossible, to summarize the characteristics of human nature, which in any case vary from individual to individual. It does, however, encompass, in transposed form, most of the responses observed among higher animals, especially those aroused by sexual desire, the love for children, the instinct of self-preservation, and the concern for daily nourishment. Moreover, these are apparent not only in the individual himself and for his own needs, but also for those of his offspring who are not yet in a position to secure their own subsistence. Man also displays the instinct to defend his living space or hunting ground against intruders.

Human behavior is undoubtedly hormonal in its most primitive form, then consciously felt and reasoned. All its manifestations are expressions of dispositions contained in the human inheritance, i.e. the "nature" of the subjects they affect.

Corporate bodies and institutions

The various interactions just mentioned give rise to organic groupings endowed with durable existence. These have their own destinies and may be assigned names that remain their own no matter what changes they undergo. Men produce, buy, sell, make war or peace, and reach decisions according to their surrounding circumstances; they respond to prevailing conditions by taking action. In other words, human societies display "behavior" whose main characteristics resemble those of the individuals who compose them.

Human societies are nevertheless quite different from human persons. They have neither a brain for thinking nor sensory organs for perceiving; they have no voice for commanding, no hands for working. They lack a body, which is always, in earthly experience, the medium of the human person.

To underscore the differences and similarities between human persons and human societies, we call such societies bodies or entities. In this context the term is obviously not used in its strictly legal sense, which refers to abstractions called legal entities. Rather, it refers to all those groups which, notwithstanding their lack of physical reality, do exist in the world and display characteristic behavior.

Nevertheless, it is true that bodies or entities can "behave" to the extent that they are provided with fictitious organs able to perform all or some of the activities which in individuals are carried out by certain physical organs. In a traditional family, for example, the father knows directly the needs and capabilities of each member. He decides, directs, and distributes. His authority is accepted by the members of the group because of the bonds of affection which unite them or because of the penalties he is empowered to apply. Thus, as head of the family, the father is at once the thinking grain of the entity he controls, its commanding voice, and, on occasion, its constraining hand. He determines the family behavior, with less efficacy certainly than he does his own, but using methods that are very similar to those which produce his own personal behavior.

Every aggregate body or entity is provided with a deciding and commanding organ which receives and processes information from without, prepares decisions, and passes them on as commands to operating units. The head of a body or entity is often an individual. Whether he is a ringleader, a monarch, a dictator, a commander-in-chief, or a contractor, he places himself at the disposal of the entity and performs on its behalf the functions that the human body performs for human persons. To extend the analogy further, the intelligence and liaison branches of a modern army might be viewed as sensory organs, the operating units as the effectuators, and the Supreme Command as the brain.

As they evolved, however, aggregate bodies and entities grew increasingly complex, like the tasks they had to perform. In the process, the decision- and choice-making organ that serves as the brain was particularly affected. The most extreme form of this transformation is evident in consensual systems which submit social decisions to complex agreement procedures: the parliamentary structures of modern states are the most typical examples. Every budget debate demonstrates the fictitious role of Parliament or Congress as a brain; it reaches a decision on the basis of information provided by the sensory organs of the state, leaving execution of the decision to the executive branch. The procedure is simpler, but very similar, in the case of modern corporations.

In every case, the very existence of a body or entity implies the corresponding existence of some "sovereignty." In its specific forms, this is the exact counterpart of the presence that characterizes the human person. No matter what form it takes, the "sovereign" is essentially the organ that integrates the behavior of all its "subjects," like the stalks of wheat in a sheaf, and thereby fashions the behavior of the entity it governs. The sovereign does not exist, of course, unless the support of the "organs" ensures the accumulation, transmission, and processing—and occasionally storage in the relevant "memories," (for instance, archives and files)—of information received from outside as well as the implementation of its desires by the executive agents under its control.

Such sovereignty is not the product of natural growth, however. It is "instituted," using methods to be discussed in the next chapter, by an explicit or tacit act of incorporation. The characteristic structures of bodies or entities are, for this reason, called "institutions."

It is important here to avoid a misunderstanding which might arise from the ambiguity of the word "institution." At times it denotes a corpus of rules of law which determine the behavior of persons subject to them, at other times the organs responsible for the enforcement of such rules. The two meanings are fairly close. We shall be using the second here.

Institutions, in this sense, obviously cannot be superimposed on previously existing entities. They are in fact consubstantial with such entities; without them, a body or entity could no more exist than could a human person without a brain.

The hierarchical structures of human societies

"Human society did not grow like a gradually expanding circle. On the contrary, it developed from small groups which, having long been in existence, gradually combined. Several families combined to form a phratry, several phratries formed a tribe, and several tribes formed a city." The members of a group did not lose their individuality in the process of association. Thus, "the city is a confederation of several groups, individuals, families, phratries, tribes, which had been formed before it and which it allowed to continue in existence."[1] These words by Fustel de Coulanges underline the particulate—that is, the "quantified"—structure of the substance of human societies. Furthermore, they confirm the social nature of human groupings: the *gens* is composed of families, the phratry of *gentes*, the tribe of phratries, the city of tribes.

The federative process continues so long as the individual issuing from the latest integration remains social. Thus cities united into confederations or *amphictyons*—Delos and Delphi, for instance—were true societies. The cities were welded by a common cult: as Strabo explained, "the same concept which presided over the foundation of towns generated sacrifices made in common by several cities." This concept also gave rise to the Roman Empire. In 340 B.C., Annius, the leader of the cities of Latium, which had united to rise from the chaos into which they had been thrown by conquest without integration, declared in the Senate, "We form one state [*una civitas*] with you!"

Thus, in human societies, just as in physical nature, there is a genuine hierarchy of levels of organization. Each particle is a society of particles belonging to the next lower level. Every combination of successive levels constitutes a hierarchical structure, but any individual may belong to several parallel structures at the same time. Thus individuals who are members of the chain of organizations composed of families, tribes, cities, and nations may also belong to a business firm, which, in turn, may be local, regional, national, or worldwide, or to a labor union within the firm, which may include the same

[1] Fustel de Coulanges, *La Cité antique*, 1960, pp. 143, 145.

levels of organization. Like physical matter, the material of human societies is particulate and is organized on successive levels.

Human societies, like all societies, are machines

Groupings of men, like all societies in the inanimate world, may be said not merely to "be," but also to "do" or "make." A married couple bears and raises children until they are capable of living independently. As the parents transmit, through training and education, the traditions they carry on, they exercise a catalytic action of the same sort as that of productive or self-reproductive cells. Similarly the *gens*, the clan, and the tribe, by means of internal mechanisms based essentially on the exercise of authority by the father, the ancestor, or the chief, impose on their members the behavior required for the pursuit of the social ends of the group. Thus integration in an organized group ensure social peace within the group, assists justice to prevail in accordance with the predominant ideology, and secures the sustenance and security of the group members by organizing joint action in the form of hunt or war.

In the same way, a city, through its services, assumes responsibility for the requirements of collective life. A nation maintains and develops the physical and spiritual inheritance which, it feels, it holds in trust. Its armies and police protect it against the external and internal dangers which threaten its existence at every moment.

The mechanical nature of economic entities is even more obvious. Industrial undertakings, workshops, farms, factories, shipping or railroad companies, banks, insurance companies, even restaurants and hotels—all produce physical goods or services. They do so by combining, under some adequate "authority," the utilizations of the materials and services required for their production.

Thus, in every instance, human societies are genuine control systems—in the mechanical sense of the word. They submit a flow of inputs consisting of matter and energy to the coalescing or processing operations that will produce the item, itself a material or a service, it is their function to produce. By virtue of their nature, which is always related to a purpose, they are the specific agents of the Promethean transformation of the universe.

CHAPTER VIII

The Modalities of Promethean Intervention

"God governs inferior beings by means of superior beings . . . in order to confer creatures themselves the dignity of being causes."[1]

Thus elevated to the dignity of causes, these human creatures steer the Promethean vessel across the sea of all possibilities. They are individuals or entities, each with its own finality and volitions which, as they materialize, tend to fulfill their aspirations and desires.

Men are free

As an epigraph to this book I used the disillusioned comment which, in Sartre's version of the myth, Jupiter, the king of the gods, addressed to Aegisthus, the king of Argos: ". . . the same secret weighs heavy on our hearts. . . . The sorry secret of gods and kings: that men are free. They are free, Aegisthus. You know it, but they do not."

The freedom Jupiter refers to here is not a legal capacity.

---

[1] *Summa Theologica*, I, xxii, 30.

It is an innate, congenital quality governing all voluntary and conscious acts and excluding therefore those which pertain to vegetative life. Of course, this freedom exists only to the extent that the physical or mental integrity of the agent is not impaired. It is the consequence of the agent's anatomical and psychic structure as well as of the nervous system which directs the use he makes of it.

Because of this structure, man does not perform the actions which make up his behavior unless he wants to perform them. He is always "in the hands of his own counsel."[2] From this point of view, neither the slave nor the soldier differs in any way from the freeborn citizen. To stir any of them to action, the person who commands or orders them must inspire them with the will to perform as he wants them to.

Every action costs its agent the sacrifices it requires and brings him the beneficial results it generates. Generally speaking, an act will not be performed unless the agent, according to his own scale of values, inclinations, and desires, considers "in his own counsel" that the benefits will exceed the cost in terms of efforts and sacrifices. To resort to economic parlance, the desirability of the former must exceed the undesirability of the latter.

Thus individual behavior is a function of the value judgements generated by the effects it achieves. Such assessments result, on the one hand, from the dispositions of the person making them—from his "makeup," his inclinations, in a word his own nature—and, on the other hand, from his information about the world in which he operates—that is to say, from the nature of things.

Thus, behavior, as the result of the interactions between the internal and the external world, between the self and the rest of the universe, is the product of a continuing dialogue between the person acting and the outside world. Hence, while

[2] Ibid., I, xxii, 2.

the Promethean revolution tends essentially to modify individual behaviors, it can come about in only two ways: either by changing the "nature" of the actors or by changing the messages they receive from the world influencing them. The first method will result in a genuine refashioning of men, the second in a refashioning of the influences of "things" external to men, including other living beings.

THE REFASHIONING OF MEN

The role of ideology

It is generally accepted that the response of non-Promethean living beings to the messages they receive from the external world is, with varying degrees of precision, determined by their innate biological inheritance. This inheritance is contained entirely in the genes of their chromosomes. Thus the genes may be said to determine the "nature" of the being carrying them. They do not, certainly, determine its form and behavior with immutable rigor. However, by limiting its responses to the messages it receives from the outside world, the genes, as the media of heredity, determine the contribution of the person himself to the process which brings about both the form and the behavior.

The Promethean mutation rests entirely on the emergence of conscious behavior in certain segments of human activity. To an outside observer conscious human behavior may be indistinguishable from certain responses that are characteristic of higher animals. But anyone who, through introspection, becomes aware of its true nature realizes that behavior, to the extent that it is conscious, is the outcome of a choice made by an individual from among all the possibles, in conformity with the hierarchy of his inclinations. The individual always seems to relate the consequences of his modest acts to a scale of values produced by his states of consciousness. But, unlike the states of consciousness of a dog or a monkey, those of man, through verbalized thought, crystalize into "ideas," which are stored by memory.

Naturally, a good deal of human behavior is not fully conscious. A great many actions are prompted by instinctive responses which are biological rather than mental. It is precisely this dual origin of human action that leads us to liken "ideas," which generate psychic structures and conscious behavior, to genes, which determine physical structures and instinctive behavior.

As a matter of fact, we know no more about how ideas determine conscious behavior than we do about how genes determine the conduct of bees or ants within their own societies. What we do know, however, is that ideas are the matrices of conscious behavior as genes are of instinctive behavior.

The total of an individual's ideas constitutes his ideology, as the sum of his genes constitutes his inheritance. Genes are more solidly anchored in the chromosomes than ideas are in memory, of course, and ideas share more of the nature of acquired characteristics than of organic structures. But again one must wonder whether, to an outside rather than an introspective observer the conscious behavior of a large number of individuals would not appear to be highly determined, like the activity of a swarm of bees or an ant colony.

Nevertheless, even though many ideologies can be regarded as acquired characteristics, they are likely to be transmitted from generation to generation through education and teaching. Furthermore, since they are as "infectious and contagious," in Jacques Monod's words,[3] as they are conquering, they are submitted to the specific processes of natural selection which affect the individuals or social groups to which they belong.

[3] Interview. *Le Monde*, December 9, 1965.

For all these reasons, while ideologies are not absolutely identical in each era for all the individuals within a given population, they are nevertheless generally held in common by a large number of individuals. Within each social group, they give rise to a dominant behavior pattern, from which individual behavior deviates just as individuals deviate from the average type of a race or a species.

The existence in every era and in every social group of a dominant ideology affects and coordinates most instances of individual behavior. Thus ideologies have come to be the most effective coalescing agents of human societies.

The integrating nature of the most important ideology, that of religion, is confirmed by the etymology of the word. As Lucretius points out, it comes from the Latin *religare*, to bind together. Some confirmation of this semantic interpretation can be found in the declaration, "I reunite . . ." which heralded the freedom of Protestants condemned to the galleys after the revocation of Edict of Nantes at the end of the seventeenth century.[4]

Because of their associative function, which is their common and primary characteristic, ideologies seem to be genuine control systems. (The phrase is used here in the mechanical and technical sense, independently of the moral implications usually attached to it.) Their mechanical aspect appears essentially in their impact on behavior: alterion of the former changes the latter. Ideologies not only "are"; they also "do" or "make." They all tend to elicit from men a mode of being different from what their own nature would have inspired without ideologies.

If you are not convinced that an ideology is a wellspring of behavior, listen to the Sermon on the Mount:

> Blessed are the poor in spirit, for theirs is the Kingdom of Heaven; blessed are the meek for they shall inherit

---

[4] André Chamson, *La Superbe*, 1967, p. 104.

the earth; blessed are the sorrowful, for they shall be comforted; blessed are they who do hunger and thirst after righteousness, for they shall be filled; blessed are the merciful, for they shall obtain mercy.

The greedy, the violent, the unjust, and the merciless, if they once believe, will not remain as they are. The Beatitudes will transform them into something else and, by altering their nature, will change their acts.

What is true of the religious ideology is no less so of all the ideologies that have competed for men's minds through history. Marxist ideology, as documented in the *Communist Manifesto*, is a no less striking example:

> The proletariat will use its political supremacy to wrest, by degrees, all capital from the bourgeoisie, to centralize all instruments of production in the hands of the State . . . and to increase the total of productive forces as rapidly as possible.
>
> Of course, in the beginning this cannot be effected except by means of despotic inroads on the rights of property and on the conditions of bourgeois production; by means of measures, therefore, which appear economically insufficient and untenable, but which, in the course of the movement, outstrip themselves . . . and are unavoidable as a means of entirely revolutionizing the manner of production.

These general principles are followed by the Marxist decalogue, which is not only a program but also a list of "commandments." That the Marxist ideology generates behavior is made perfectly clear by the applications of it in totaliitarian states, especially in Soviet Russia since 1917.

In the same way, *Mein Kampf*, the true bible of Nazism, gave rise to the various aspects of Hitlerite behavior. Even purely economic ideologies, such as that of the physiocrats or Keynes's *General Theory of Employment, Interest and Money*, have directly shaped the behavior of large populations.

The analogy between genes and ideas as matrices of behavior is particularly striking in those borderline cases where ideologies tend to counteract behavior which is of an indisputably biological nature. Aggression is a general characteristic of those species which have succeeded in surviving and prospering. The Gospels have worked to counter it by teaching meekness and humility. But the effect—admittedly more physical than spiritual—of a tranquilizer like chlorpromazine on certain species, such as fighting fish (*Bella splendeus*, the fighting fish of Siam) or man, is similar in nature, if not strictly analogous.[5]

The close intermeshing of physical and moral realities, which does not of course confuse the two, transforms the ideas that determine moral behavior into powerful tools for modifying the natural results of the biological influences that determine physical behavior.

The birth, life, and death of dominant ideologies

One aspect of the natural history of ideologies is that they are subject to beneficial or perverse changes followed by phases of development or regression, occasionally by death. In general, the changes or mutations take place in the brain or brains of one or more men, and the question of their origin raises the same problems as the origin of those mutations that affect the inherited legacy of living beings: are they determined by some supernatural will—that is, "inspired" or "revealed" —or are they fortuitous?

The question is particularly relevant to the most important, the oldest, and most widespread of all ideologies: religion. This is apparently so intimately connected with the biological nature of the human mind that it could be considered innate. The dawn of reflective thought in man brought him face to

[5] I owe this piece of information to my colleague Professor Delay.

face with the insoluble problems of evil, suffering, and death. His demand for intelligibility in all things, which seems to be an immanent characteristic of his nature, apparently led him to the notion of a transcendental cause. Only that could account for the inexplicable, make the intolerable bearable, and bring about the events he wished for in the face of indifferent or hostile Nature.

> The natural course of things is not something which is immediately and readily understandable to man, but something which he understands only because he has made it intelligible. . . . From the very beginning, man, faced with the usual phenomena occurring in the universe, had a feeling that there was a cause behind them and endeavored to discover the originator. This quest for causality, which was already looming up in the times of cave drawings, is still to be found among primitive peoples, for whom the purpose of prayer is to unleash favorable causations.[6]

As Emile Durkheim explains:

> Every year plants die; will they come back to life? Animal species tend to die out as the result of a natural or violent death; will they be renewed in due time and in adequate conditions? Rain is particularly unpredictable: sometimes it looks as if we were never to have rain any more. All these periodical weakenings in Nature point to one thing, that the sacred beings who control animals, plants, rain, etc. seem to go through critical stages during such periods: thus they too have their times of weakness. But man cannot be an indifferent witness to these events. If he is to live, universal life must continue and, consequently, the gods must not die. So he struggles to support

[6] Father R. P. Schmidt, quoted in R. Aron, *Le Dieu des origines*, Paris, pp. 27, 28.

them, to help them, and, to that end, he mobilizes all the strength at his command and places it at their service. The blood in his veins has fecundating power: he will shed it. He will draw the germs of life from the sacred stones of his clan, and scatter them in space.[7]

But man's primary confrontation has been with the mystery of death. No matter how far back into the history of the Indo-European race one goes, one finds that people have never accepted that after a short span of life, everything is finished for man. Burial rites have come down from even the most ancient civilizations:

> Before imagining or worshiping Indra or Zeus, man worshiped the dead: he was afraid of them, he prayed to them. This seems to have been the origin of religious feeling. Perhaps it was at the sight of death that man first had the notion of the supernatural and nurtured the hope of something beyond what he could see. Death was the first mystery; it put man on the path to other mysteries. It raised his thoughts from the visible to the invisible, from the ephemereal to the eternal, from the human to the divine.[8]

> At least a hundred thousand years ago those strange creatures called Neanderthal men ceremoniously buried their dead, providing them with arms and tools.[9]

Religious feeling pervades the minds of even the most primitive men. As the direct product of their rational exigencies, it appears to be fundamentally linked to the existence of their minds. I should like to keep this remark free of any controversy about the natural or supernatural character of the religious

---

[7] *Les Formes élémentaires de la vie religieuse*, p. 492.
[8] Fustel de Coulanges, *La Cité antique*, p. 20.
[9] Gordon Childe, *De la Préhistoire à l'Histoire*, 1963, p. 28.

attitude or the revealed or inspired nature of knowledge of the divine. The statement that faith is the product of the rational exigencies of the human mind does not solve the problem of the supreme explanation; positing such needs in man's mind inevitably raises but does not answer the question of the origin of that need and its universality.

Problems raised by the development of secular ideologies are different but of the same nature. An idea germinates in the mind of one man or in the minds of several men. It is usually extracted from the "Brownian motion" of thought which Pierre Auger has described. But this description does not solve the transcendent problem for secular ideologies any more than it does for religious ideologies: is it chance or inspiration that serves every writer, thinker, and artist as, each morning, he culls the fruit of his nightly thoughts?

Like a seed in rich earth, an idea develops, grows, and bears fruit if it finds adequate nutrients in the mind which receives it. We have all experienced the shock of recognizing the idea that will solve the problems with which we have been struggling. All the other ideas—and they are many —decay and die.

When man developed the means of communication derived from articulated speech, along with the techniques necessary for storing and reproducing thought, it became possible for the originator of an idea to transmit oral or written signs and messages in order to stimulate in his fellows ideas more or less analogous to his own.

It is not a matter of inspiration or spontaneous appearance, but of the catalytic formation, in a suitable set of circumstances, of an existing being by another, similar, existing being. . . . To a certain extent, the man who receives the message can accept or refuse to consider the idea. This capacity to choose is often quite weak, however: once a message is understood, an idea forms almost inevitably. Thus, a population of ideas composed of many species, constantly prepared to reproduce themselves and to overwhelm individual members of the population, especially the young or new members, when they are susceptible, is superimposed upon a human population whose members regularly exchange signals.[10]

It is through such a process of reproduction and multiplication that an idea, when it falls on fertile ground, generates an "ideology."

The conservation of characteristics is not guaranteed here, as it is in the realm of living beings, by those well-defined and self-reproductive molecules which multiply indefinitely in suitable media. Those particular species that are called "ideas" are therefore far less stable than animal or vegetable species; many mutants are constantly emerging in their host humans or during the process of transmission from one individual to another. . . . As a consequence, every human population will harbor representative samples of several varieties of an idea which has previously emerged or been introduced. Some choice—analogous to the natural selection process —among such mutants is inevitable, and the criteria for this choice will govern the ensuing evolution. Just as in biological genetics, two kinds of factors will be operating: some are internal and depend upon the degree of stability or facility of reproduction; others are external or somatic and result from selection operating not on the ideas but on their host humans. A dual process of adjustment takes place: the adjustment of ideas to the characteristics of the men in whose brains they will multiply, and the adjustment of the men who are the media of ideas to the environments in which they live. . . . In this way certain ideologies, which are vigorous and prolific, are selected,

10 Pierre Auger, *L'Homme microscopique*, pp. 130–131.

148

and the men who harbor them tend to spread over the entire world. No account is taken of the individual satisfaction of such men, provided that they thrive and continue to welcome such ideologies.[11]

Thus construed,

an ideology, judging from all the evidence, is a social product; it owes its power and its influence to the fact that it has been accepted by society. If every member accepts them, apparently absurd beliefs become ideological, and it never enters anyone's mind to doubt a universally held belief.[12]

The fact that ideas do not become ideologies unless they have been widely accepted explains the close mutual dependence which is established between economic or social conditions—the environment of most members of society—and the dominant ideology. Karl Marx identified this dependence and noted how widespread it is. He was thus led to view ideologies as a "superstructure," the necessary by-product of the conditions of production. The same phenomenon also accounts for the existence of class ideologies, which are closely related to the conscious or unconscious interests of the individuals who are their media.

The growth of ideologies has profoundly altered the mechanics of the evolution of social groupings which are typical of the human species. Human societies are no longer transformed by mutations in their biological inheritance, but by the evolution of their ideologies.

Despite all this, ideologies experience the process of attrition that affects all existents. They are endlessly assailed by rival ideologies and, like animal species, survive only to the extent

[11] Ibid., pp. 132–134.
[12] Childe, op cit., pp. 30–31.

that they confer strength and endurance upon the group which is their medium. In 1620 Sir Francis Bacon founded experimental empiricism by recognizing that the prerogatives of Nature endowed human reason with new power. Men found that it was by obeying Nature that they could command her.[13] As a result of the Baconian revolution, the hierarchy of ideologies was changed: all the others yielded universality and dominance to scientific method.

But the increasingly rapid refinement of instruments and methods of observation hastened the evolution of physical facts, just as progress in sensitiveness and constant shifts in the balance between opposing forces quickened the evolution of social facts. The acceleration of history was simply the consequence of a heightened rate of change in dominant ideologies.

This change in pace has not affected the nature of the sway of the evolutionary process, however. It was mainly by imposing new ideologies on certain groups of men that the sons of Prometheus could submit large populations of individuals to genuine "reconditioning," a process equivalent in many ways to rebirth. Thus, the progenitors of ideologies acquired the power to modify the "creation" in which they lived. Having become "creators"—or, rather, "re-creators"—they themselves pioneered the future Promethean evolution of the universe.

Sowing and cultivating ideologies

Our earlier statement that ideologies are contagious and conquering was misleading. Though their originators, adepts, or disciples tend to propagate them, their Promethean ends will be fulfilled only to the extent that ideologies persuade an increasing number of minds. To impose a new ideology on an individual, the scale of values which determines his acts

---

[13] See *Novum Organum*, I, xxi ff.

must be changed. His tastes and desires must be transformed. In short, a new "nature" must be imposed on him by means of education.

Educational methods run the whole gamut, from training systems based on the theory of conditioned reflexes to moral and intellectual principles which call upon the loftiest qualities of mind and heart. Love in all its forms—love of God, love of country, love of one's master, physical love, intellectual love—creates in the heart of the person who feels it the desire to emulate and obey, itself a source of moral responsiveness.

The mystical reverence with which a believer submits to God, the love of a son for his father, the physical attraction uniting lovers, all generate between the partners the feeling of an indissoluble union. The submissive partner, in his hunger to obey and serve, is led to substitute for his own scale of values the one imposed upon him by the authority he reveres. Eventually, as an educated or trained individual, he will unconstrainedly choose to perform actions which, previously, he had not regarded as the most desirable: "If ye be led of the spirit, ye are not under the law," as St. Paul said in his epistle to the Galatians.

To the man led by the spirit, however, it seems as though love or faith has actually changed his nature, to the point where he freely and spontaneously desires what his God or his beloved desires for him.

The next chapter will show that religious practice inspired in men the behaviors which—starting from the biological reactions resulting from consanguinity—generated the first social institutions: "Primitive religion, after having enlarged and extended the family, formed a larger association—the city . . . and gave it its principles, its rules, its usages, its magistrates. All the institutions of the ancient peoples originated in it."[14]

As I contemplate the processions of so many children to

---

[14] Coulanges, op. cit., p. 4.

school each morning, or of millions of men each week to their churches, temples, or mosques, I think of the vast reconditioning enterprise which teaches men to burn what they once worshiped, and to worship what they once burned.[15] It alters their scale of values, drawing them up out of the biological mire and lifting their eyes toward the heavens. The human plant, taught and trained, is to untutored man what the garden rose is to the wild briar.

RECONDITIONING "THINGS"

The need for compelling action

Education and propaganda may be efficient, and faith and love may be eager and sincere, but no ideology has ever relied on them alone to control men's minds and to govern individual behavior fully. Every attempt to convince has always been supported by some compelling action likely to reinforce the motivation an individual derives from his ideas, his love, or his faith. In fact, to intensify the reasons for choosing or discarding behaviors that an individual would, in certain circumstances, adopt as a result of his convictions or tastes—i.e. of his own "nature"—the desirability or undesirability of each of the acts within his capabilities must be altered, but with no change in his convictions or tastes.

The desirability or undesirability of any action is related to its aggregate effect on the individual who performs it. The effect can be modified only by the accretion to the principal results of the act of such secondary results as rewards or penalties. Their desirability or undesirability will be added to that of the principal result.

[15] St. Remy, as he baptized Clovis, King of the Franks, is according to legend supposed to have adjured him: "Burn what you once worshiped, and worship what you once burned." [*Trans.*]

If the secondary result is indissolubly linked to the principal result, each individual who remains unchanged will adjust his behavior. The adjustment will depend upon the way he views the aggregate outcome of the action, within the actual conditions for its accomplishment. Such behavior will no longer be determined merely by the consequences of an action, as generated by its intrinsic nature, but by its consequences as adjusted by the rewards or punishments that may have become attached to it.

Thus, by systematically modifying the affective consequences of an action for the person who performs it, by adding negative or positive sanctions (whether punishment or recompense), it becomes possible to compel an individual, whose personality is otherwise left intact, to change his behavior. Where they apply, penalties or rewards added to the consequences of an action actually recondition the nature of things surrounding an agent. This reconditioning imparts to ideological education the supplemental efficiency that enables it to affect the behavior of all individuals, even those whose faith or deepest beliefs are not strong enough to outweigh the powerful biological remnants because of which they are "only evil continually." [16]

To reduce the frequency of theft, for example, the use of, or even the simple coveting of, other people's property is made liable to punishments that will be considered highly undesirable by the majority of those individuals whose consciences would not otherwise forbid them to steal. Thus a compelling pattern is created: coupled with a number of years of imprisonment as punishment, the theft of an automobile will no longer appear desirable to anyone who, even after his character has been fashioned by education, might still desire that automobile.

To the extent that a compelling sanction has been adequately tailored and is universally applied, it enables the promulgating

---

[16] Genesis VI: 5.

authority to regulate at all times and in all circumstances the behavior of all individuals except those who are abnormal. The compulsion can be evaded only by inveterate sinners, who are so attracted to misdoing that they disregard the sanctions linked with it, or by individuals whose intelligence is too dim to enable them to perceive the relation between present pleasure and future sanction.

The five sources of compelling action

Any compelling sanction consists of a desired or undesired influence indissolubly linked with the accomplishment of an act. As such, this linkage affects the aggregate desirability of the consequences of the act. There are, therefore, as many forms of compulsion as there are sources of influences that the individuals they affect will find desirable or undesirable.

MIGHT

The simplest form of compelling action is that exercised by the strong vis-à-vis the weak. By exerting his power, a strong man can inflict on anyone weaker than himself painful, and essentially undesirable, sensations; he is therefore in a position to direct as he wishes the behavior of a person under his domination. This form of compulsion generates savage societies, which, in their natural state, present a disheartening picture.

Promethean intervention tends to resist this sort of compulsion. To that end, it has consistently endeavored, by subjecting the strong to a social constraint, to prevent them from subjugating those weaker than themselves for their own selfish ends. It operated in this way to convert savage societies into humane societies.

DIVINE AUTHORITY

If a believer does not derive sufficiently strong motivations from his love for his God to offset those that stem from his desires or passions, his faith can strengthen them. The reward promised to men who comply with the Commandments is as desirable as the punishment threatened to those who break them is undesirable.

Compelling desirability may lie in the joy granted in this life or the next, and compelling undesirability may lie in suffering inflicted before or after death. But promises of reward or punishment do not actually affect behavior unless the believers are convinced that the one or the other will effectively be applied to them and that they cannot be evaded them by craftiness, fraud, or deceit.

Hence, for a man of faith the desirability or undesirability of an action is no longer inherent in the consequences of the act alone. It is associated with the entire complex formed by the consequences of the action and whatever recompense or penalty is linked with it. By such means divine authority exerts a compelling force to impose upon man compliance with the Commandments taught him by revelation or through the prophets.

CONSCIENCE

While compelling action is especially apparent in theocratic societies, it is no less obvious in those societies that appeal to the moral sense of individuals to achieve compliance with certain rules of behavior. Indeed, when sound individuals obey the principles of ethics which their conscience has taught them, they enjoy the desirable sense that they have fulfilled an obligation, just as they experience the undesirable feeling of remorse when they violate those principles. Thus the moral sense causes them to desire the performance of actions imposed on them as an "obligations," regardless of the nature of the inherent consequences.

The canons of such a moral sense are not as exacting as divine commandments and teachings. But their essential features do tally in almost every respect—to such an extent, indeed, that one may wonder whether they have an autonomous existence or whether they were perhaps stamped on the wax of the human conscience by the religious mould which formed it.

HUMAN JUSTICE

Although the compelling influence of moral sense is in many ways analogous to that of religious faith, it nevertheless lacks the same degree of efficacy, at least insofar as the great majority of men are concerned. For this reason, the social authorities have had to rely upon another form of compelling action. They themselves administer it directly in those societies where religious faith is no longer universal and all-powerful or when they wish to influence actions not controlled by the divine will.

Such social compulsion is exercised either through the addition of desirable features, such as civil honors, promotions, and decorations, to certain actions or modes of behavior or—and especially—through the imposition of undesirable restraints, decided by judicial bodies and made effective by a coercive force, i.e. the police. Such sanctions and restraints are organized and controlled by the public authorities.

Judicial coercion relies on undesirable effects on an individual's honor, his possessions, his liberty, and sometimes even his life. It becomes effective as soon as the relevant authority learns that a prohibited action has been performed. Justice will be efficacious and society will be effectively policed if, in each and every case, the undesirable effect of an act forbidden by the social authorities outweighs the desirability of the reward that would be gained by performing it.

The price mechanism

The recompense-and-sanction system is implemented in a

specific way, but over a very wide field, in the form of the price mechanism. To every seller the price serves as recompense for the sacrifice he makes by depriving himself of the object sold; to every buyer, it is the sacrifice he must accept in exchange for the satisfaction expected from the object purchased. The recompenses and penalties brought into play by the price mechanism, unlike those on which religious, moral, or judiciary authorities rely, are strictly quantitative and subject to very fine variations. In some monetary markets, for instance, interest rates—which are the rent paid for the use of money—vary by as little as $1/64$ of one percent.

In general, prices do not depend on the individuality of the buyer or the seller. Each individual confronts a market price which, except where a monopoly or oligopoly is involved, he cannot influence directly. However, he considers this price in relation to a scale of values, which is his and his alone. At each market price level, an individual will offer to sell those goods he owns whose loss seems to him less undesirable than the cash he would derive as proceeds of the sale seems desirable. Conversely, he will demand those goods whose possession seems to him more desirable than deprivation of the corresponding amount of money, as a result of the payment of the price, seems undesirable.

Thus, every price movement acts like a sluice gate controlling the potential supplies and demands that are likely to have access to the market. In this way, it determines with the utmost sensitivity the behavior of all possible participants in the market.

Economists have demonstrated theoretically and ascertained in reality that—unless a ceiling has been officially placed on prices or trusts or cartels are present—the price of any article for which market demand is in excess of supply will rise. Because this movement will endure as long as the cause has not disappeared, it cannot fail—at least as long as prices remain free—to bring about, with full efficiency, equilibrium between supply and demand in the market under consideration.

In more general terms, however, supplies and demands are mere intermediate stages in causal sequences that culminate in the activities of production and consumption. Thus the decisions made by buyers and sellers exert a determining influence on the economic and social structures concerned. By virtue of the fact that it vests in those who operate in the market the power to fashion the whole of the production system and determine its functioning, the price mechanism is the most accurate, efficacious, powerful, and widespread instrument of Promethean intervention.

It is clear that the compelling intervention—whether it is divine or human, whether it relies on present or future punishment or recompense, whether it inflicts physical, moral, or simply financial penalties or rewards—always operates according to the same procedure: it modifies the consequences of the acts it tends to alter. It is efficacious (if it is) because, in every instance, man remains his own counsel. All things being equal so far as his desires are concerned, his conduct, insofar as it is deliberate, is determined in relation to the results it might possibly yield for him.

The conditions of efficacy for compelling action

If, as an institution, a compelling penalty is to influence behavior, individuals tempted to perform the prohibited act must be convinced that its performance will inevitably bring about the result linked with it.

Under theocratic systems of coercion, this is achieved by one of the essential attributes of divinity: the ability to learn, through supernatural powers, all men's acts, whether open or hidden, and even their intentions and the thoughts which inspire them before they have been translated into acts. The Roman Catholic Church furthers such knowledge by the confession which the individual makes to a priest. As God's representative on earth, and empowered by Him to remit sin, the priest is actually the medium through which the divine verdict is expressed. In other, more secular religions, confession is known as "self-criticism."

Under systems which vest the exercise of coercive authority in moral conscience, the necessary inquiry is ensured by the fact that man cannot prevent his own conscience from passing judgement on his acts. In vain did Cain try to escape from the scrutiny of the eye which had witnessed his crime; neither wall, nor tower, nor covering archway could protect him. And when he eventually turned to death for relief from the remorse pursuing him, the eye was in the tomb watching Cain.

In legally established societies, the party suffering injury initiates coercive action by lodging a complaint. The action may be public or private, depending on whether the interest of a private person or that of the community is at stake.

If coercive or constraining action is to be efficacious, two conditions must be met: the intervening authority must be able to convey to a potential malefactor the certainty that his crime will in any case be found out and that the penalty attached to it will be meted out to him; and the punishment must be strong enough to make the prohibited action undesirable, no matter how desirable the consequences might have been, if gained independently. This second *sine qua non* requires that the undesirability of the result far outweigh the desirability of the act in the eyes of anyone who might be tempted to undertake it because of what he expects to gain from it.

This will be true in a theocratic society, for any man who fears God dreads His punishments and desires any rewards He may give. In societies based on morality, remorse, on the one hand, and the satisfaction of having fulfilled an obligation, on the other, will be sufficient for all those who heed the voice of conscience. In legally established societies, the penalties enacted by the social authorities—fines or punishments involving loss of liberty or life—will fail to catch only the forbidden actions carried out by individuals who hope to evade compelling action by craftiness or trickery, or by those who consider that the punishment, as a mere future possibility, presents a minor degree of undesirability. Finally, in the field of economics, the price mechanism will be effective to the extent that both buyers and sellers are aware that the action they have in mind can materialize only at the market price. This condition implies the impossibility of violent action or fraud and an effective ban on groups of buyers or sellers, such as monopolies, trusts, or cartels.

The law as an instrument for the implementation of any system to constrain individual wills

If compelling undesirability is to wield the influence for which it has been established, it must be a decisive factor in the struggle between volitions from which every act emerges. This condition cannot be met, however, unless a person who might perform an act knows beforehand which actions will bring on punishment and which will escape it. Punishment cannot serve as a motivating force, therefore, unless the conditions under which it may be applied are clearly and openly defined and are known to everyone whom they might affect.

Theocratic systems fulfill this requirement through revelation, which informs man of the rules with which his behavior must comply if he is to escape God's wrath or reap the rewards promised to the just. These rules are embodied in "commandments" and in teachings which are the word of God and make known His will. In societies based on ethics, the rules governing the use of constraining action are revealed directly and immediately by the voice of conscience, which, in every case, tells men what their "duty" is. As already noted, however, the dictates of conscience do not have, in the minds

160

of most people, the clarity and rigor of God's commands. In legally established societies, judicial intervention is governed by regulations of which "ignorance is no excuse"; these clearly set forth which actions are lawful in each case and which make their authors liable to the severe reprisals of the secular arm.

Thus, whether they have a theocratic, moral, or judicial basis, all systems of constraint or coercion share one characteristic: they define those actions whose performance will bring about the undesirable constraint. In this way they indirectly define the area in which an act may be performed with no consequences to the actor except those inherent in the nature of things. Within this area every individual can make his own decision in full freedom, solely on the basis of those consequences and in terms of the desirability as he views it. Within such an area, his action will in no way be constrained.

It is therefore clear that every commandment, rule, or law divides the realm of the possible into two distinct areas: an area where action is freely allowed, in which man determines the course of his choice with full freedom and solely in terms of consequences of his acts, and an area of forbidden action, where any intervention makes him liable to undesirable constraint. In the area of permitted action, man is said to have the "right" to act, while in the area of forbidden action he is denied such a right. Thus commandments, laws, and regulations define the "rights" of those to whom they apply; each right provides only a certain leeway to act as outlined by the constraining authority. The right to own, think, write, or believe does not in any way imply ownership, thinking, writing, or belief, but only the assignment of areas in which man is free to own, think, write or believe as he wishes.

Where the law establishes an area of free action, it does so by establishing the limits of the area of constrained action. Its establishment of the former automatically sets limits on the latter and outlines the task of the constraining authority, whether religious, moral, or social. Right as defined by law is therefore not merely freedom to act as outlined by the constraining authority; it also includes the criterion for the intervention of the latter. Because of this dual feature, it is the primary tool of government in human societies.

Commandment and inducement

Equipped with these two means of intervention—the conditioning of men and conditioning of things—the constraining authority, whether divine or human, can use them in different ways. It can make any act which is different from those it orders him to perform so undesirable that an individual will voluntarily forego those actions he would have performed, if in no danger of suffering constraining punishment; conversely, he will decide to perform those he would not have chosen to accomplish in full freedom but which the constraining authority commands him to perform. There is nothing different here from the ordinary mechanism of behavior. The acting individual continues to rely upon only his own judgement. But in order to escape the constraining punishment that is meted out to those who disobey, or to win the reward promised to those who obey, he decides of his own free will to abide by the "commandments."

The power of such commands can apply to virtually all the actions an individual can perform in full freedom. The individual then becomes a slave. But if it applies only to certain lines of action, the agent becomes a soldier or a subordinate. Where it applies to moral behavior alone, it generates the faithful of a Church or the members of a political party.

The relevant authority can, however, forego the mass application of constraining sanctions and rewards. Used in a moderate way, they simply add their desirability or undesirability to the natural consequences which an action produces for the person performing it. In this case the acting individual no longer decides on the basis of the natural consequences of an act, but in the light of those consequences as supplemented by the desirability or undesirability which the constraining authority superimposes. The actor is no longer commanded to perform the actions the authority expects from him but is induced to perform them. Apart from the divine or human systems of rewards and sanctions, the most characteristic form of this inducement system is in the price mechanism.

The two systems, command and inducement, have equivalent effects but differ profoundly in their operation. A command obliges an individual to desire what the constraining authority wants him to desire, whereas inducement leads him to decide of his own free will to perform the actions expected of him by the constraining authority. The first system is termed authoritarian, the second liberal. Both, however, cause the individual to perform those actions that the constraining authority has chosen for him, whether under command or of his own free will. Thus command and inducement direct and transform the energy of the acting individual. The operative "devices" that accomplish this—religious faith, moral conscience, police, justice, the market—are therefore monitoring or control systems. That is to say, they are genuine machines, like the mechanical equipment which converts a flow of energy without changing its magnitude but imposing on it the form intended by the machine builder.

Rewards and sanctions modify the field of interactions surrounding the acting individual. The space in which he lives and acts is no longer what it was before the intervention of the constraining authority. Interactions within it are affected, and, thereby, the behavior of individual particles is altered. Thus, as we complete this analysis, we are faced once again with the procedures which the sons of Prometheus have used to bring about a situation wherein Nature is no longer what she was before their intervention but what they want her to be.

The creative process in nature and society

This analysis has demonstrated that "Promethean creation" is effected either by means of modifications in the person and the emergence within him of a new scale of values, or through modification of the influences brought to bear upon him by the things in the world surrounding him. In the first case, the particle itself is changed; in the second, the field of interactions that surrounds it.

Considering these two forms of modification and the consequences they have on the field of interactions which generate behavior, it is clear that the individual apparently ranges over the entire field of possibles open to his choice and chooses from among them his own path, increasing to the utmost the difference between the satisfactions and sacrifices which will result for him. I do not for a moment claim that the particles of the inanimate world determine their behavior in a similar manner. I only wish to point the resemblance, despite the profound differences involved, between the terms used by the natural sciences and those used by the human sciences to describe the process which extracts the present from the realm of all the possibles. Such extraction creates, at every instant, that reality which is engulfed into the past.

CHAPTER IX

The Rise of Promethean Order in the Universe

"Order is mind finding itself in things"

SECURE IN THE powers described in the preceding chapter, the sons of Prometheus, as the media of certain ends, computers of emergence, and masters of the energy reserves of the universe, set out to reshape the Jupiterian order upon which they had been established. Their constructions never began with a *tabula rasa*, but always from some preexisting order, whose layout they changed and refined as they wished. To this end, they used existing but purely potential interactions, conferring efficacy upon them through appropriate juxtapositions while instilling into the newly created groupings those quantities of energy without which they could not have existed.

• This was not, however, simply a random alteration of layout. It was wrought by individuals or global entities prompted by the desire to elicit from the new order the satisfaction they know it could yield. "Order," said Bergson, in his *Creative Evolution* "is a certain accord between subject and object. It is mind finding itself in things." Thus the Promethean

165

construction was intended to bring the universe closer to what its transformers wanted it to be.

But the transformers were no more free in their creative effort than the gods. They could use only the interactions that resulted from the nature of things and the energy reserves made available to them by the "Prometheus incident." Hence they could reap order only in the field of the possible. In each epoch, the limits of this field depended strictly upon the interactions whose existence the Promethean creators had identified and the energy reserves they were able to use with the techniques they controlled. The potentialities that could materialize, therefore, depended directly on the current state of knowledge; every discovery opened to creative activity new possibilities which could materialize if invested with matter or energy.

The feet in the biological mud and the face turned toward the sky

Promethean creators can bring into being only possibilities, but they activate merely a small portion of those. The possibilities they summon into existence are chosen because the resulting benefits outweigh the sacrifices involved in their creation. The choices that call forth the real from the potential and that create the Promethean universe to come, selecting from everything that could be, are dictated by each Promethean creator's preferences, tastes, and scale of preferences.

In the last analysis, the Promethean creator's "nature" is the one factor that determines the structure of his creation from among all possibilities. But the nature of the Promethean creator, as we know it from our own consciousness and that of our fellow beings, encompasses, in all its complexity, contradictory aspirations. It is dominated by those profound instincts which seem to tend toward the conservation of the life of the individual or of the species in the unending struggle for the survival of the fittest. Think only of those characteristics that must all be present in a being if it is to survive (films about animal societies give some idea of them): the instinct to win the means of survival, by no matter what or how brutal a method; the hunger for possessions which compels the defense and expansion of the familial domain; the sexual instinct which impels the male to seek the favors of the desired female; love of self and love of progeny, with eagerness to transmit "inheritance" to them; ambition; the will to power. All these appetites are directed toward the same end, the enjoyment and disposition of the goods desired.

But enjoyment and disposition are not feasible until and unless these goods, like a bone a dog takes to his kennel, have been secured against competing appetites. The hungry dog that wins the coveted bone is the strongest one—or the one who successfully posed as such. Thus every individual uses strength or deceit to stake out his own area for enjoyment and disposition. And he can hold onto that area only to the extent that he remains the strongest or the wiliest.

The ascendancy of might extends not only to inanimate objects, but also to those useful and therefore desirable things, like men and beasts. Might cannot, of course, interfere with a man's mastery of his own body, which is congenital. But constraint can make any actions he may choose to perform which are not commanded by his master so undesirable to him that he will resolve of his own accord not to perform them: he then becomes a "slave."

Thus the weak, in the natural state, will inevitably lose their freedom. Only those who can find in their own strength—or in the protection they can secure—the means of deflecting any influences which would bring them into subjection will escape slavery. The state of nature is a perpetual contest of strength, in which the weak will be subjugated and deprived of all those goods which it will not be in the interest of the less weak to leave to their enjoyment and use.

Horror at this natural state appears to be felt in the animal kingdom only by those individuals that are its victims, and only when they are about to experience its effects in their own flesh. A steer in a truck on its way to the slaughterhouse gives no appearance of pressing its claim to life. Lack of conceptual thought prevents it from imagining in the abstract the brutality whose effects it does not yet feel.

But the dawn of reflective thought confronted men with the insoluble problems of evil, suffering, and death. Some of them, uplifted by transcendent influences or motivated by the first stirrings of dawning rationality, were endowed with the ability to imagine and even experience the sufferings of others. This seems to have awakened a revolt against the purely biological determinism of animality and the search for means to escape it. Such a desire for change—whether selfish or altruistic; the product of material, moral, or spiritual demands; the reflection of the very various aspirations motivating human creatures or the result of their birth, history, education or economic status—is the hallmark of the Promethean attitude.

A universe of machines

The Promethean order superimposed on the Jupiterian order is always finalized. It never limits itself to mere "being," but strives to "do" what men expect and hope from it. This "doing" is effected by the juxtaposition of particles of matter and energy incorporated into durable structures; these, in turn, generate, directly or indirectly, the goods or services desired by men. And it is the purpose of the control systems known as "machines" to effect such juxtapositions.

The production of machines is always, directly or indirectly, catered to human consumption, which is in fact its unique object and supreme end. Look about you: whatever has been created by men is, in its basic nature, a machine for the production either of goods and services for human consumption or of machines that will produce such goods and services. A ploughed and fertilized field is a Promethean machine, as are the plough and the ox pulling it, the cow that transforms the grass in a meadow into meat and milk, and the automobile or airplane which transports men to where they want to be and goods to the places where men want them. Similarly, a dwelling provides housing services and is a Promethean machine, as is the winch that helped in its construction. Apparel provides the services of clothing and is a Promethean machine, like the loom that produced the cloth from which it was made. A painting, a poem, or a symphony which produces aesthetic pleasure is a machine constructed by the sons of Prometheus to provide men with the beauty they long for. All human groups—business undertakings, armies, cities, and nations—are Promethean machines, because all of them produce desired goods or services.

Some Promethean creations spring directly from alterations or proliferations of the Jupiterian creation by means of additional matter or energy. Chlorophyll is not a Promethean product, of course, but its diffusion through pasture grasses or in the salad we eat is a product of that essentially Promethean intervention known as agriculture. In the same way, the family and the married couple are constructed along Jupiterian lines, but in their Promethean form they are profoundly altered by the commandments of religion, ethics, or law. Even man's body and brain, though produced by nature, are affected deeply by Promethean intervention, as expressed through physical, intellectual, or moral "culture."

However, whether Promethean or Jupiterian, man's body is the first machine, since it is the progenitor of all the others. Thus there is no doubt that the Promethean universe is an immense collection of machines made by men for men. Machines are the instruments of men's power and an inexhaustible source of the structural adjustments through which they continuously recreate the world. In all his glory, Prometheus is a machine builder.

The religious and authoritarian matrix of Promethean order

Human societies are machines in the sense that they "make" what isolated individuals cannot: the child is the product of a married couple; hunting or war is the product of tribal groups; the Great Pyramid of Egypt is the product of a collective human machine composed of 100,000 pairs of arms, equivalent to about 10,000 horsepower.

The creation of machines consisting of living beings is not an exclusive Promethean privilege, however. There are innumerable animal societies. They too maintain social peace between their members; they construct collective habitations, like the hive and the anthill; they store provisions for the winter; they defend their territory against possible invaders. But these societies are based on biological interactions, the direct results of the inherited patrimony of their members.

Promethean mutation has changed the associative influence. By making psychism the source of conscious behavior, it has entrusted the coordination of individual activities to ideologies reinforced by constraints. Ideologies and constraints had to be extraordinarily powerful, however, if they were to unite beings only recently risen above the level of pure animality and to establish between them bonds as strong as those the sexual hormones establish between a married couple, or lactation in the relations between a mother and her cubs. The worship of a common ancestor—a feeling undoubtedly very close to biological attraction and, in any case, certainly halfway between mere biology and psychology—has provided the bond maintaining together primitive societies. Fustel de Coulanges explains:

> We find it among the Chinese, as among the ancient Getae and Scythians, and among the tribes of Africa as among those of the New World. . . . What unites the members of the ancient family is something stronger than birth, sentiment, or physical force: it is the religion of the hearth and the ancestors.[1]

Despite this bond, the family, enclosed within the limits of its own consanguinity, could not supply the strong "machines" required for the defense of its territory or the construction of cities. The preservation of the same religion by several lines of descendants ensured the extension of the family cell, which included everyone who worshiped a common ancestor in the same manner. (The ancestor was the first man laid to rest in the tomb and to whom his descendants offered the funeral meal.)

In Rome, the *gens* developed as an enlarged family group, with its own priesthood, its own code of justice, and its own internal government. Domestic religion forbade two families to mix or coalesce, although it was possible for several families to unite in the celebration of a cult common to them all without sacrificing aspects of their religions. Such unions formed a family molecule which was called a *phratry* in Greek and a *curia* in Latin.

The associative processes then continued, always in the same way. Several curiae or phratries combined to form a tribe, which in turn had its own religion, and each tribe had an altar and a protecting god of its own. The tribe took its name from its protecting god; for that reason, the Greeks called him the "eponymous hero."

Just as several phratries combined into a tribe, so several

---

[1] Fustel de Coulanges, *La Cité antique*, pp. 35, 40.

tribes associated to form a city. Hence the progressive formation of larger and larger integrated units was accomplished by successive aggregation, on gradually higher "levels of organization." The social link which had been biological at the outset, became psychological—i.e., a common belief in transcendental beings, a religion which bound together groups which had previously been independent.

If some experimental verification must be added to the testimony of history, one need only observe that there would be no villages on the earth if there were not towering steeples around which the houses huddle. Because it had recourse to some transcendental power, religious society carried within itself the seed of command. The ancestor, divinized as an eponymous hero or the god of the city, retained all the powers with which he had been invested when, as a living person, he had commanded the destiny of his group.

But men must be informed of the divine command. The prophet, inspired by the divinity or serving as the repository of revelation, acts as the supreme magistrate on its behalf: "The domestic hearth had its own high priest, who was the father of the family; the curia had its curile or phratriarch; each tribe had its own religious leader, and the city had its pontiff." This priest of the public hearth was called the king or, in Greece, the *archon* or *prytanis*. "Just as, in the family, authority was inherent in the priesthood, and the father, as head of the domestic cult, who was also judge and master, so in the city the high priest was also the political leader."[2] He was magistrate, judge, and military commander. The Kings of Sparta, according to Aristotle, "performed sacrifices, waged war, and dispensed justice."[3] Similarly, at Rome, "a consul was something rather more than just a man; he was the intermediary between man and the divinity."[4]

[2] Ibid., pp. 202, 206.
[3] *Politics*, III, 9.
[4] Coulanges, op. cit., p. 212.

However, if command is to generate organization, it must not only be expressed; it must also be carried out. In this respect, the faithful encountered no problem. They would carry out the divine will because they wanted to serve it—or to reap the rewards promised, in this world or the next, to those who complied with its commands—or because they wished to escape the punishment meted out to those who disregard them. As for the halfhearted, the lukewarm, and the unbelieving, the authority of the god-king was reinforced by the coercive power resulting from the penalties which administrative and police authorities applied to delinquents.

But to establish a legal system authority must have access to devoted agents who are prepared to act as the instruments of its decisions. The faithfulness of these agents cannot be the result of coercion, of course, because there is no such thing as self-coercion; it can come only from faith in the word of the master. The power of the king, whether he was a god or a prophet of the god, could be effective only insofar as it was supported by a group of faithful who respected the divine will and were prepared to enforce it. Thus, around each authoritarian government whose will must be known and felt on even the lowest levels of the people there must be a nucleus of militants—clergy or party members—who are convinced of the truth of the dogma and who are eager to ensure its application.

The union of priesthood and power in the same person is hardly surprising: "We find it in the beginnings of almost every society whether it is because, in the infancy of nations, only religion can elicit obedience, or because our own nature feels it necessary never to submit to any command but that of a moral idea."[5] Every government's concern for legitimacy can unquestionably be explained by the need for moral investiture. Whether it is provided by heredity, "divine right," or

[5] Ibid., p. 206.

the people's approval, it confers on sovereignty the efficacy which is the *sine qua non* of its reality.

These views are illustrated by Lewis Mumford's study of the government machinery which made it possible, during the third millenium before our era, for the pharaoh, a divine king, to construct the Great Pyramid of Egypt:

> The workers who carried out the design . . . had minds of a new order: trained in obedience to the letter, limited in response to the word of command descending from the king through a bureaucratic hierarchy, forfeiting during the period of service any trace of autonomy of initiative; slavishly undeviating in performance. . . . It was the king who uttered the original commands: it was the king who demanded absolute obedience and punished disobedience with torture, mutilation, or death; it was the king who alone had the godlike power of turning live men into dead mechanical objects. . . . What was needed was a special form of transmission gear: an army of scribes, messengers, stewards, superintendents, gang bosses, and major and minor executives, whose very existence depended upon their carrying out the king's orders, or those of his powerful ministers. . . . In other words, a bureaucracy: a group of men, capable of transmitting and executing a command, with the ritualistic punctilio of a priest, the mindless obedience of a soldier. . . . The importance of this bureaucratic link between the source of power, the divine king, and the actual human machines that performed the work of construction or destruction can hardly be exaggerated. . . . This administrative method requires studious repression of all the autonomous functions of the personality. . . . A similar constraint constitutes the psychological aspect of the systematic subordination which brought the labor machine into existence.[6]

[6] Lewis Mumford, "The First Megamachine," *Diogenes*, 55 (July-September 1966).

This analysis demonstrates that a Promethean order—the human machine which constructed the pyramids, for example —vests conception and choice, and therefore will and decision, in the person of the god-king. He is the sole depository of authority and sole master of the behavior of the human particles constituting the social machine. These human particles submit to the will of the master either through faith or through constraint. In either case, they are controlled as a machine is by its operator; they are deprived of freedom of thought and action—that is, of the fundamental attribute of the human person.

The "long march" of the human person

The presence in all archaic societies of an authority spontaneously or constrainedly accepted by all their members coordinated individual behavior. By controlling the acts of his subjects, a leader, whether he was prophet, king, chief of a clan, or head of a family, was able to prohibit mutual aggression and war between them. He used his command to ensure that the various tasks, no matter how difficult, were apportioned and carried out; he determined consumption and investment according to the quantity of goods available. In short, he designed and brought into existence a social order. This achievement could be accomplished, however, by only annihilating all freedom of choice, and hence all liberty, in his subjects.

The subjects had not, of course, surrendered their power to do only what they wanted to do (this is an innate characteristic of human nature). But this faculty had been inhibited by the ideology they served or by the coercive apparatus that enforced it.

In some primitive social groups, every individual who is not king is ignored. His "existence" is an anatomical fact but remains a social virtuality. "Among primitive peoples like the

Kanakas," Maurice Leenhardt explains, "a man is not aware of his own existence; he cannot apprehend it."[7]

A study by Marcel Mauss shows how recent the philosophic terms "self," "category of the self," the "cult of the self," and "respect of self" are. . . . Archaic existence was a consensual existence, in which each member, in Lévy-Bruhl's phrase, was part of everything and everyone. The center of interest, the significant unit, was not individual life, but the social order as a whole, defined by mythic traditions and codified by rituals. The community's *a priori* conceptions provided some sort of pre-set pattern which excluded individual initiative. The whole pattern of life was like a stage setting which has been ruled by the gods from the outset; compliance with the scenario ensured the smooth functioning of the world, within which it behooved each individual scrupulously to perform the part assigned to him.[8]

Thus, though the individual did exist, certain of its faculties were paralyzed by group pressures, as is the case in a number of animal societies. Only those individuals who, on various levels of organization, determined modes of being, thinking, or acting retained their autonomy, whether they were gods, prophets, tribal chiefs, or the heads of clans or families.

In such a society all other individuals see their human capacities mutilated to some extent. They are aware they have within themselves the possibility of a psychic life of their own, but they feel that nothing they can do will bring it into the world where other men live. Subjected to individual or collective constraint, and limited in every avenue of thought or action which is not the one the group intends to impose, they actually cease to be themselves, becoming instead what the social authority wishes them to be.

[7] Maurice Leenhardt, *Do Kamo*, N.R.F., 1947, p. 84.
[8] G. Gusdorf, *Signification humaine de la liberté*, 1962, pp. 18–19.

It is from this sort of collective domination, in a certain region of the world, during a certain epoch, and under certain historical circumstances, that the individual, responding to the pressure of the capacities which he felt had been vested in him, struggled to free himself. "In the history of western consciousness, Socrates symbolizes the change in the pattern of authority which shifted from the world of mythical traditions to the universe of rational critique and independent judgement."[9] Spartacus led the revolt against the stifling of the human personality, but it was the Christian revolution which gave all men, no matter what their origin, an immortal soul. It refined the human person out of the collective lode in which it had been imprisoned, whether it was a horde, a tribe, or a *gens*. Though slaves were not masters of their own bodies, Christianity, dawning after the Stoics, recognized that they had their own souls: "There is neither bond nor free . . . for ye are all one in Christ Jesus."[10]

The distinction between soul and body restructured the concept of person on an ideological and metaphysical basis. The body was the "machine," the matrix of all human machines, and the soul was the mysterious presence which gave it life.

From that point on the power that conferred upon living beings "the dignity of being causes" was no longer strength, heredity, or enthronement but the presence of conscious psychism in them. This is the characteristic feature of the human person. Throughout the entire West it has never ceased pressing against all collective structures, against every sort of "alienation" that would hinder its realization.

Once the seed had been sown, the plant grew before man's very eyes. However, it developed at different rates in the various regions of the planet, depending to a great extent on the beliefs and myths on which the seed had fallen. Even

[9] Ibid., pp. 21–22.
[10] Galations III: 28.

in the least favorable areas, however, the person can be seen to press against the resistance of the groups. The person's will to be is the underlying cause of the Promethean conquest of the universe.

The imposition of social peace

Violence is the first cause of alienation. By threatening coercive actions, whether real or potential, it can constrain persons who are in no position to defend their independence—either with their own strength or with the strength of whatever protector they may have secured—against the demands of their master. Violence has the power not only to force the weak individual to relinquish the enjoyment and use of whichever of his possessions the strong want, but can also force him to order his own body, of his own free will, to make only those gestures that the master commands. The person still exists, but it is subjected to the will of another: it has simply become a slave.

As it grew in self-awareness, Promethean thought came to realize both the horror and the absurdity of the savage state. The characteristics of the human person in a subjugated individual may not have been totally annihilated—Epictetus affords evidence of that—but they were inhibited in their creative function. The person who had them was reduced to the same condition as one who did not have them.

Even the free individual was obliged to devote all his physical and intellectual activity to the quest for daily bread and to the protection of the goods whose use and enjoyment he desired. Most of this human faculties and talents were absorbed by this offensive and defensive struggle. It seemed as though his life had not been endowed with other faculties, especially those of disinterested creativity. Hence man was prevented from being what he could have been, what his Creator had. intended him to be.

Faced with such an unnatural situation, Prometheus took

up the challenge as soon as he appeared in the world of men. He was greatly assisted by the gods, who generated social structures, and by the pontiffs, who were their representatives. The action of the gods who had created the city was a mere extension of the techniques that had maintained social peace in animal societies: there is no internecine warfare in a beehive or an anthill, any more than there is in a family or in a tribe where the father or the chief is obeyed. But blind submission to the authority of a leader, whether it is the result of purely biological behavior or the effect of an accepted or imposed social discipline, considerably limits the development of the human person.

Furthermore, as a society expands, its controls over behavior which is not of a purely biological nature must be relaxed. Effective neutralization of the natural aggressiveness of the individuals or entities which social bonds unite soon becomes fully or partly impossible. Moreover, the pacifying influence of the group can operate only within the society; it is unable to prevent war between non-social persons or entities, such as states which do not belong to the type of society called a "league of nations."

For all these reasons, Prometheus was induced by the rise of the human person and the enlargement of human societies to find methods of social pacification which would impinge less on individual liberty. They would be more suitable for ruling large societies than blind submission to the authority of a leader, whether he was god, king, or father.

THE PRINCIPLE OF A PEACEFUL SOCIETY[11]

To the extent that war is the outcome of conflicting claims to the enjoyment and use of the same thing, a society will be peaceful when enjoyment and use of that thing are desired,

[11] I have already expounded the following consideration in *L'Ordre social*, 3rd ed., 1967, chap. XXXII, iii.

in those conditions in which they can be obtained, by only one person.

For such a society, to exist, it is necessary and sufficient that the enjoyment and use of things which are in themselves coveted by men be made undesirable for any person other than the one who has been selected to obtain them. Thus the problem of establishing a peaceful society can be reduced to the application of a particular system of social constraint, a system that ensures that only one person has the right to use and enjoy a certain thing at a given moment.

A system of this sort is applied by the constraining authorities, who endeavor to impose social peace upon men against their true nature and regardless of their wishes.

THE VARIOUS FORMS OF PACIFYING CONSTRAINT

We have already seen that peaceful systems of coercing intervention may be based on religion, moral conscience, law, or economics. In each case the constraining authority will succeed in creating a state of peace among men to the extent that it ensures strict partitioning of their claims to enjoyment and use of the goods desired.

In theocratic societies, men are forbidden by divine will to take or even desire the goods of another. Moses received these two commandments from God on Mount Sinai: "Thou shalt not steal. . . . Thou shalt not covet thy neighbor's house; neither shalt thou desire his wife, nor his servant, nor his handmaid, nor his ox, nor his ass, nor anything that is thy neighbor's." Similarly, the seventh and tenth commandments forbid any act or desire impinging upon the goods of another: "Another's goods thou shalt not take or keep deliberately; nor shalt thou covet them to have them unjustly."[12] In the face of these prohibitions, the God-loving or God-fearing man cannot desire riches that are not his own, no matter how desirable they may seem in themselves since he does not want

[12] Exodus 20:15, 17; Deuteronomy 5:19, 21.

them, he will not attempt to get them. All rivalry and, therefore, all war between men will be averted. Thus the Scriptures establish social relationships on the basis of a strict assignment of individual sovereignties. So long as this distribution is respected, there can be no conflict of influence; peace will be granted to those men on earth who are of good will.

In societies based on ethics, it is conscience that disapproves of the taking or coveting of another's property. It balances the desirability of any action that would tend to acquire that property against the remorse that would result from the misdeed. Wherever the voice of conscience is heard and obeyed, nothing can be desired by more than one person. Here again peace among men has been imposed.

In legally established societies, judges determine and the police carry out the punishments that apply to those who attempt to use and enjoy their neighbor's property. If the laws are adequate and the police system efficient, the use and enjoyment of any possession will appear undesirable except to its rightful owner. Rival claims to property will no longer disturb social peace.

This analysis of the procedures which establish and maintain peaceful relations among men is confirmed *a contrario* by observation of the circumstances in which they might revert to a savage state. A weakening or the disappearance of religious faith, the absence of any moral sense, the lack of courts for deciding and police for enforcing regulations—all these would give free rein to men's so-called natural tendencies. These would then be free to unleash war and reinstate the natural conditions. The constraints of civilization would prevent these developments more effectively by being both severe and severely applied.

PROPERTY RIGHTS: A NECESSARY INSTRUMENT FOR THE
ESTABLISHMENT AND MAINTENANCE OF SOCIAL PEACE

All those systems which aim at imposing social peace upon

men, even against their will, are based upon the same principle: the subordination of every object to the will of one person only. This exclusive assignment of the use and enjoyment of a particular thing to a single individual is known as the right to property. Whoever enjoys this right has complete freedom of action regarding the object; all others are under the obligation to abstain fully. Thus property rights subject every object to one single owner. As far as the individual is concerned, it divides the universe into two parts: the area of possession, in which he rules, and the rest of the world, where he is, except by consent of the owner, powerless.

Within the realm of possessions, each individual freely acts to resolve his actions according to the desirability, for him, of their consequences—and on that basis alone. Outside that realm, his acts are subject to constraint. No matter how desirable they may seem to him, he will be induced not to desire such acts because of the coercive penalties associated with them. Thus the right of ownership establishes social peace by eliminating from men's hearts not only the desire for the possessions of another, but also the possibility of coveting those goods in the conditions in which they could be secured.

It has often been claimed that the right to property is a tool of selfishness and the result of theft. In fact, ownership is unaffected by the process out of which it evolved and the resulting distribution. But it must be noted that its consequences can be, and in fact are, largely corrected by the systems of income redistribution that most modern governments apply.

In itself, the right of ownership has no other goal than social peace. In this respect, it is significant that every decalogue, every code of law, established it and that every civilizing system has relied on it. Even those systems of government which authorize only collective ownership for certain possessions cannot ignore it. On the contrary, they reinforce its strength by punishing violations of public ownership more severely.

Certain critics, more politically than sociologically minded have been surprised and almost indignant to find that I regard the right to property as an instrument of social peace. They consider it a tool and symbol of inequality, injustice, and unrelenting conservatism. I invite them to reflect on the analysis in these pages and to question whether peace could be granted to men apart from these two alternatives: an authoritarian control of individual behavior or a system of general and efficacious appropriation. One must accept the former or the latter.

Moral order

Peace achieved through the establishment of property rights generates a social structure within which each "owner" freely chooses and controls the content of his rights. At every instant the order thus established will be molded by the wills of the individuals or aggregate entities, whether public or private, in which fate has vested rights of ownership. Each of them exercises control over that part of the universe which corresponds to the area of its rights.

Within such a system, however, the resolves that will shape the world order must emanate—directly in the case of individuals, and indirectly in the case of larger entities—from men of whom God saw that their "wickedness was great in the earth, and that every imagination of the thought of their heart was only evil continually."[13] A world that had merely been pacified would be a world of homicide, lust, and lies; a world of selfishness and hatred, of desperate inequality and slavery; a world where only the aspirations of "owners" were satisfied, with utter disregard for the persons of the propertyless and no concern for the immediate or future interests of the community.

[13] Genesis VI:5.

Such a social structure could not fulfill the expectations of some of Prometheus's sons—the serfs, the slaves, the free men bereft of all property—who felt within themselves, clearly or confusedly and despite their social condition, the presence of a human person with potentialities equal to those of the property owners. Nor could it satisfy those sons of Prometheus who owned riches but were capable of imagining the suffering of those that were destitute. Such men, in their eagerness for equality and justice, would never consider that the peace brought about by the establishment of property—the creation of a society dominated by the principle "A place for everything and everything in its place"—afforded a sufficient solution to the social problem. It could not enable them to identify themselves mentally with reality. Furthermore, in their view it conferred upon social order the character of moral disorder.

However, if peace was to be safeguarded—i.e. if war was to be excluded from human relations—the partitioning of individual sovereignties which had arisen out of the appropriation of all desired possessions had to be maintained.

Yet if the world was not to be shaped by the will of property owners alone, there was only one choice: to impose upon them a modification of the behavior which they would have adopted within their own rights had they been left free to behave as they chose. Authority could not rest content with simple pacification; it had to alter mores—that is, to impose upon men a code of morality that counteracted their own nature and inclinations.

Prometheus set about establishing a moral order by adapting to the coercive and constraining procedures mentioned earlier the end he had in mind. At first, men were subject to only two authorities: might and their gods. As soon as the former had been eliminated, for free men, by the institution of property rights, there only remained the latter. "It was the constant consensus among the ancients," says Fustel de Coulanges, "that every man's obligations were toward his gods only."[14]

So Prometheus at first used the influence of the gods to alter individual behavior. However, the will of the gods was communicated to men through fully human personalities—prophets, lawmakers, social reformers—who were themselves taught the divine will by revelation or inspiration.

In the words of St. Thomas Aquinas,

> Two things make up Divine Providence, the conception of order according to which things are directed toward their end, and the achievement of that order. . . . As regards the first of these functions, God sees to everything directly and immediately. As for the second, there exist intermediaries for Divine Providence, because God governs inferior beings through the agency of the superior ones.[15]

The clearest type of theocratic government would seem to be that whose origin and structure are described in the Old Testament. Moses receives God's word amid thunder and clouds on Sinai. He rules the people because he has been chosen directly by God, who has commanded him to say to the children of Israel: "I hath sent me unto you." His government is highly centralized, composed by choosing "able men out of all Israel," and making them "heads over the people, rulers of thousands, rulers of hundreds, rulers of fifties, and rulers of tens. And they judged the people at all seasons: the hard causes they brought unto Moses but every small matter they judged themselves."[16] God's commandments outlined the task of government in every detail, defining all prescribed and all forbidden acts, out of all the actions possible

---

[14] Coulanges, op. cit., p. 246.
[15] *Summa theologica*, I, xxii, 30.
[16] Exodus 3:14, 18:25, 26.

to men. Omission of the former or commission of the latter brought down divine punishment.

The substance of these commandments (excluding social peace by prohibiting actions affecting the property of others) can be divided into two main categories. The first consists of those rules aimed at modifying the use of free men's sovereignty over their own bodies; they prohibit murder, lying, false witness, adultery, while enjoining filial love and observance of the Sabbath. Because they have pronounced effects on morals, they are essentially of a moral nature. The commandments in the second group tend to modify the use made by "property owners" of their sovereignty over beings and things other than themselves. They cover, in the greatest detail, the situation of slaves, widows, and orphans and the use of things borrowed or lent. By enjoining charity, they affect the use and enjoyment of personal wealth.

In a general way, Jewish ethical principles tend to modify the will of the master of a person or owner of a thing by changing the sum total of the results he shall reap from all the acts it is within his power to accomplish. God's Ten Commandments, a renewal of those brought down by Moses from Mount Sinai, set forth the fundamentals of Christian morals. In addition, the Gospels brought into full light the law of love and charity. This is no longer simply one of the many expressions of the divine will, but, along with the commandment to love God, contains "all the law and the prophets."

The divine teachings complete this corpus of instruction by enjoining men to rise above their natural tendencies. They are to love the poor, despise riches and honors, and revere obedience. Respect for the human person, regardless of any considerations of rank, social class, or nationality, is to become the basis for all social relations.

It is worth considering for a moment the enormous gap between the social climate which the divine tends to establish and the "natural" state which human nature, left to itself, cannot fail to bring about. To make love rule supreme among men who, in the natural state, hate one another; to impose charity on men who are naturally motivated by selfishness; to ensure that they are constantly struggling against the gravitation of their nature toward lying, lust, and murder—in short, to create a habitable world out of the hell which men's natural instincts and desires would create—these ought to be the goals of the constraint imposed by the divine will upon the wills of men.

Although the substance of moral teaching seems to derive from religion, some men nevertheless have a more specific form of conscience. A moral conscience attaches to certain actions the pleasures of having fulfilled an obligation and to others the pains of remorse. I shall not attempt to determine whether the moral conscience is a somewhat inherited human trait or simply a mark left by thousands of years of religious teaching. In any case, there is no escaping the fact that, altogether, the principles of secular morality are very similar to the commandments of the Decalogue. Furthermore, in the majority of cases they are less constraining than the divine commandments.

As religious faith ceased to be universal and its influence on men's behavior weakened, and as the development of sensitivity increased the social exigencies of the community, governments realized that they had to support with their coercive and constraining action those religious teachings aimed at humanizing the distribution of wealth. To this end they instituted new commandments, called social regulations, and used them to control certain areas of life which scripture had left to individual free will. Thus, public assistance obliges taxpayers to use part of their income for charitable purposes. In the same way social security programs, when not entirely supported by contributions from their beneficiaries, impose on the community, and hence on its individual members, the need to participate in the maintenance of the elderly and the easing of the suffering that results from sickness and disease, accidents or unemployment. All such systems force individuals to use their resources in a way which is different from what would have been most desirable to them.

Similarly, modern governments correct apparently unwarranted inequalities by establishing, for example, minimum wages. They also remedy what they consider excessive accumulation of capital by graduated levies on income or wealth. Estate duties, in particular, make possible considerable modifications in the distribution of wealth, compared with the pattern which would result were the deceased owners free to transmit it in the way that appeared most desirable to them.

While the moral order tended to safeguard the human person, it could not tolerate slavery, serfdom, or bondage. To this end it was bound to outlaw the ownership of man by man. The elimination of slavery and serfdom made it impossible for anyone to exercise property rights in respect to a human person. But it also forbid a free man to place his bodily person at the unlimited disposal of another person, even if he wanted to do so, or to enter into arrangements that might force him to do so. Thus such regulation makes it impossible for any individual to relinquish those rights of enjoyment and disposition—hence of ownership—of his own body that are naturally vested in him.

The problem here is similar to the one that legislative bodies had to resolve when they decided that certain things must remain the property of certain individuals. Thus they declared that certain objects essential to living and various tools and instruments essential to work were unassailable. Another French law (passed on July 12, 1909) states that family property is similarly unassailable; by establishing the entail system, the law ensured that certain estates would remain in the ownership of certain families.

In each of these cases, as in the suppression of slavery,

the law restricts the freedom of disposition inherent in the right to property. It imposes a certain definition of such a right upon the holder of the right, even though he may consider a different definition more desirable.

The problem of slavery is useful in this context because it raises basic questions that are analogous to those encountered by any civil government seeking to safeguard human dignity. Every employment contract, in fact, deprives a worker of the free disposition of his body to the extent provided for in the contract. A long-term or indefinite contract can establish a status very close to slavery. Hence the laws of most countries declare all such contracts to be null and void.

Also, the conviction has spread that human dignity, not to mention physical health, can be impaired by unduly long hours of daily work, which exclude the necessary rest and the leisure required for moral and intellectual development. Thus the civil governments of most modern states have put a limit—eight hours—to the duration of the work supply allowed daily. Such a limitation obliges men to use their bodies, which they may fully enjoy and use as they like, being free men, in a manner that may be different from the one they would have chosen freely. The laws regulating paid holidays, weekly rest, women's and children's employment, all impose similar adjustments for ethical reasons.

The legal order

The distinction between the legal and the moral order is a matter of emphasis. Both aim at making human society different from what it would be if it were left to human deliberation exempt from any outside influence, divine or human—that is, on a purely biological level. They attempt to establish social patterns which are more congruent with human thought than natural, or savage, societies would be. Thus they serve as instruments of Promethean activity.

Like morality, law relies on the three types of Promethean intervention (divine, ideological, constraining) to impose upon men regulations governing human behavior as well as interpersonal relations or the orientation of persons toward their property. But, while both law and ethics are equally normative—and therefore Promethean—they do not share the same degree of generality and unconditionality. Modern law is farther away from the divine commandments and therefore less absolute and more human in its source.

In primitive societies, however, law is not distinct from morality. Both are divine commandments. "Law was enactment of religion, a revelation made by the gods to the ancestors, to the divine founder, to the magistrate-priest."[17] The Mosaic law, for example, is characterized by the extreme detail of its commands. It not only provides for supernatural punishment ("visiting the iniquity of the fathers upon the children into the third and fourth generation of them and showing mercy into thousands of them that keep the commandments") but also specifies the strictly human sanctions which God's representatives are to impose for each transgression. In such a context, ethics is scarcely distinguishable from law.

It was only in Rome that the development of society began to separate law and morality. The patriarchal regime, the product of inherited religion, gradually dissolved into a civil regime:

> This change in society brought about another change, this time in law. Just as much as the eupatrids and patricians were attached to the old religion and, therefore, the old law, the lower class hated that hereditary religion, which had prolonged their inferiority for so long, and that old law which had oppressed them. Not only did they detest it; they did not even understand it. Since they did not share the beliefs upon which it was based, they considered that law to be without foundation. They

[17] Coulanges, op. cit., p. 365.

found it unjust, and from that moment it became impossible for it to survive.

If we look back at the time when the plebs took on a new dignity and entered into the body politic, and compare the law at that time with the ancient law, we can see the serious changes which developed. The first and most striking was that the law had been made public and known by everyone. It was no longer that sacred and mysterious chant that was recited from one period to the next with a pious respect, that the priests alone wrote, and that only the men of pious families could know. Law left behind ritual and the books of the priests; it shed its religious mystery; it became a language which everyone could read and speak.

But something even more serious became obvious in the codes of law. The nature of the law and its foundation were no longer what they had been during the preceding period. Hitherto law was a phase of religion, a revelation made by the gods to ancestors, to the divine founder, to the magistrate-priest. In the new codes, on the other hand, the legislator did not speak in the name of the gods; the *decemvirs* of Rome received their power from the people; thus the people invested Solon with the right to make laws. The legislator therefore no longer represents religious tradition but the will of the people. Since that time, law's principle has been the popular interest, and its fundament is the assent of the majority.

Two consequences flow from this. First, law no longer has the aspect of an immutable and indisputable formula. As it became a human enterprise, it recognized that it was subject to change. The Twelve Tables of the Law declared: "What the will of the people has proclaimed, that is the law."[18]

The other consequence was this: the law, which pre-

[18] Livy, VII, 17; IX, 33, 34.

viously had been a part of religion and was consequently the inheritance of priestly families, was henceforth the common property of all citizens. The plebeian could invoke it and demand justice. The most that one can say is that the Roman patrician, who was more tenacious and devious than the *eupatrid* of Athens, tried to hide from the masses the forms of procedure; nevertheless, these forms themselves soon came to be disclosed.[19]

With Christianity, however, the cleavage between ethics and law deepened:

> Jesus Christ taught that His kingdom is not of this world. Because it was no longer terrestrial, religion mixed as little as possible in the things of the world. "Render unto Caesar the things that are Caesar's, and to God the things that are God's." That was the first time anyone had distinguished so clearly between the State and God. . . . Christianity was the first religion not to claim that law depended upon it. . . . Thus law was independent; it could draw its rules from nature, from the human conscience, from the powerful notion of justice we all have. It could develop at full liberty, reform itself and improve without any obstacle, follow the progress of morality, yield to the interests and social requirements of succeeding generations.[20]

Once its commandments had been secularized, laws as means of enforcement could also be secularized. It totally relinquished the constraining power of supernatural recompense and punishment and gradually emancipated itself from the domination of conscience. Henceforth it was to rely on judicial and police activities alone.

As the secularization of law separated it from ethics it also submitted it to the evolution of the ideas and attitudes of

[19] Coulanges, op. cit., pp. 364–365.
[20] Ibid., pp. 461–463.

the majority, i.e. of politics. The system of ownership, of welfare measures, of social security, changed. Under the influence of legislative procedures, law developed into a powerful instrument for the revision of structures; it was capable of making them even more constant with the demands of those whose fate they ruled.

The economic order

If the moral order is the outcome of an orientation of the behavior of a human being with regard to himself and the order of law—mainly of his behavior in relation to other human beings—then the economic order is the result of the orientation of the behavior of human beings in the administration of their earthly habitat, including its planetary and possibly its stellar extensions—that is to say, all the goods the universe has placed at their disposal.

Economic behavior materializes outside the human person through the acts of production, consumption, or investment each individual performs, either directly or by means of the machines at his command.

The economic order is natural (or Jupiterian, according to the terms used earlier) to the extent that it is produced by human beings who determine how they will behave according to their own nature—that is, independently from any religious, moral, legal, or governmental constraint—in the light of the possibilities opened to them by the presence of the beings and things which surround them in their natural state. This order will become Promethean when the thought it expresses tends to be found in things; in order to be realized, it will determine individual behavior through the processes of Promethean intervention discussed earlier.

Any theory generating economic order will be designed to establish a certain form of production and a certain type of distribution. But if the desired order is to become a reality, it must not demand anything in excess of existing wealth; otherwise, it could not be realized. In other words, as the economic order establishes those structures of production that are considered best, it must respect the various states of equilibrium that are the prerequisites of its own existence.

Because it is the realization of theory, any economic order is necessarily planned. The only questions are at what level and by whom it is planned. The answers depend upon the modes of Promethean intervention and, more basically, upon the power it exerts over the actors in the economic realm.

In a totalitarian regime—i.e. under a system where the authorities control all economic behavior—the planning is on a full scale. By assigning a role to each agent, the system outlines the entire complex of economic structures. If the plan is to be efficiently operated, its authors must have accurate information about the production capabilities available to them, and their stipulations must be obeyed by the innumerable individuals who act in the realm of economic life. To this end, the plan must provide, in relation to the scale of values of the planning authority, for the optimal use of all possibilities.

The increasing complexity of economic structures makes it more and more unlikely that economic policies can meet such requirements. They imply that all elementary activities must be coordinated. Hence qualitative and quantitative choices are increasingly numerous and arbitrary.

However, the greatest obstacle to the development of economic totalitarianism is the progressive liberation of the human person. If a plan was to be effective, it had to be respected. This requirement implied that all economic activities would be submitted to the will of the planning authority. At a minimum, the distribution of manpower would be directed by the authorities, and consumption would be rationed.

The rise of the human person resulted in the generalization

of property rights and the suppression of slavery and serfdom. From then on, goods which a person did not own could be obtained only with the consent of the owner, hence by trading. The market had come into existence. Market prices varied until, in each sector, the quantity supplied met the demand expressed at that price. This price variation had two consequences: it oriented production capabilities, because at every moment prices moved upward or downward until they reached the point where the quantity of foods supplied equalled the quantity demanded; it brought about a balance between supply and demand, leaving no demand unsatisfied. Thus the will to acquire was extinguished because, being satisfied, it no longer had any object.

Contrary to a widely held opinion, the mechanism of the market does not in any way preclude the satisfaction of collective needs. The state and public authorities or agencies can intervene on the demand side of the market, thus influencing that portion of the productive sector that corresponds to their part in the aggregate demand. The market establishes the structure of production which gives each rational demand that content which is most desired; it is the instrument of a kind of genuine universal suffrage in the economic field.

But the market is criticized on the ground that such suffrage is restricted. Each demand affects the market only in proportion to the amount of resources which the demander is able to command. The determination of economic structures is the common object of both the planning operations and the functioning of the market. Their underlying difference lies in the authorities through whom theory "tends to find itself in things."

In a planned system, the theory that creates economic structure is that of the planning authority, it acts very much like an economic Providence:

The proper disposition of things demands that nothing

be left in disorder. . . . God carries out His plan in its smallest and finest details thanks to lower powers, through whose instrumentality He Himself operates, just as universal and superior power works through the intermediary of a lower and particular power.[21]

These lines were certainly not written with the economic order in mind, but they nevertheless are fully relevant to the providential mission of the planning authority.

In those sections of the French National Plan that concern the private sector, the authority limits itself to information and recommendations, leaving to entrepreneurs the burden and responsibility of decision making. But if a plan is really intended to outline the whole complex of economic structures, as is the case in totalitarian countries, this task is so enormous that no system—apart from those which were used in rudimentary economies or in some family and tribal groups—would dare to assume such full responsibility. Therefore, all plans have relied on the price mechanisms to some extent.

Nevertheless, it is true that in certain situations the planners have often assumed for themselves the power to fix prices authoritatively. Prices then became their instruments to prompt producers and consumers to adopt the behavior required by the plan.

In a market system, on the other hand, prices are determined by the free interplay of supply and demand. The supply, at each market price, is the quantity of goods whose possession is regarded, by each of the persons in a position to supply such goods, as less desirable than their sales proceeds. Similarly, the demand, at each market price, is the quantity of goods whose possession is considered by each of the persons in a position to demand such goods, as more desirable than the undesirability of the payment demanded.

These concepts are unwieldy and difficult to express. They

---

[21] *Summa Theologica*, III, lxxvii.

indicate how deeply price mechanism has thrust its way into the psychology of each of the eventual agents in the market, generating even the most unpleasant decisions and curbing even the most eager desires. By taking into consideration individual dispositions, no matter what they may be, and all the circumstances of the situation, the price mechanism thus brings about optimum use of production capabilities. It also generates a balance between all sectors of the market.

The book of the second genesis

By profoundly rearranging the structure of the universe, the Promethean intervention daily imposes upon it a new birth.

At first this intervention tended to modify men and groups of men—that is, individuals and aggregates alike—through evolution or mutation in those psychic genes we call ideologies. Thus reason, the prerequisite for efficient action, and morality, the strength which inhibits the biological aggressiveness so deeply embedded in human nature, were progressively established and disseminated among all the sons of Prometheus.

The modification of human material stimulated the gradual development of social groupings. These evolved from the couple and the consanguineous family to the clan, the city, the nation, and, currently, unions of nations. At the same time, and within other social hierarchical structures, there were developing groupings organized for military or economic purposes, such as troops of slaves or free men, agricultural or industrial enterprises, national or international trade unions, trusts, and cartels.

The persons or societies of persons thus organized undertook to reshape the material universe. By controlling matter and energy, they created the enormous population of objects that crowd our horizons. All these objects are machines, because directly or indirectly, they are intended to produce the goods or services—food, housing, transport, education or training, intellectual or artistic enjoyment—desired by men. Thus the Promethean creation is a vast "ordering" of the elements of the universe. It is intended to secure from the universe the needs the Promethean creators express both for themselves and for those whose destiny they command.

At this point, the sole remaining task is to identify those Promethean creators.

PART IV
The Gods and the Kings

As the epigraph of this book I cited the observation that, according to Jean-Paul Sartre, Jupiter the King of the Gods made to Aegisthus the King of Argos: "I made you in my image—a king is a god on earth. . . . We both make order reign, you in Argos, I in the world. . . ."

Certainly order prevails both in Argos and in the world. And it is inevitably produced through the integration into permanent societies, by means of appropriate interactions, of large populations of particles of existence, such as corpuscles, cells, plants, animals, or human beings. There is a vast difference between order in Argos and order in the world, however, though both are highly improbable.

The order that prevails in Argos is conceived and desired by specific men: those, in fact, who have the power to influence individual behavior and thereby to impose upon the societies generated by such behavior the structures of their choice. These are the men—sons of Prometheus in that they enjoy the sovereign power of intervention on the various levels of organization—known as "kings" in the area of their own sovereignty.

But the order that prevails in the universe exists no less certainly. The "organizations" that express it attain a very high degree of complex-

ity. Every day science provides new information about the interactions on which such organizations are based and about the nature of the processes which sustain them. Apart from transcendental interpretations based on revelation or inspiration, however, we know nothing about this order's finality. Indeed, we do not even know whether it has any finality.

The "gods" have declared themselves, or have been declared, the authors of these orders which are not the outcome of men's volitions. In order to conform with mythological tradition and to avoid choosing among rival divinities, I have placed these structures, which are independent of human volition, under the aegis of Jupiter.

Moving from the simple to the complex, I shall first consider those orders which are willed by men and whose secret is partly known to them. I shall then turn to the great mystery of those orders which exist independently of any human volition.

CHAPTER X

The Kings

The nature of royal power

A KING DOES NOT take direct action. From his throne he rules over those individuals and aggregate entities which are his "subjects." It must be noted, however, that his power is not based on a *tabula rasa*. Most of those he rules—especially those individuals as well as entities of a quasi-biological nature, such as parent-child or mother-child groups, which are close to an animal state, or tribal groups, which are more or less similar to many animal societies—are the outcome of a previous evolution in which the king had no part.

Thus royal power is confronted with preexisting orders. The king's power attempts to modify these orders in order to submit them to the exigencies of his own thought and to bring them into greater harmony with the structures his thought has prompted him to desire.

To this end, he must transform the individual behavior which generates social structures. Such a change can be effected only by control systems (in the mechanical sense of the term) formed by government machinery. Such control systems consist essentially of ideologies, the direct sources of the behavior of persons endowed with psychism, and constraining interventions which, as a result of rewards or penalties applied to certain actions, can modify the behavior they generate without altering ideologies.

The king is the individual who monitors control systems. Through them he has the power to make society something other than its constituents would have made it had they been free to act according to their own nature—that is, without the imposition of any ideology and free of any constraint. Instead, the society becomes what he, the king, wants it to be. Thus royal power acts positively in generating structures which would not exist without it, whether they constitute new levels of organization or modify preexisting structures on already established levels of organization.

The religious origin of sovereignty

It is worth giving some thought to the enormous difficulty primitive populations had in founding organized societies. Social bonds are not easily established among human beings, who are so free, so different, so elusive. In order to give them a common code of regulations, to institute commandments and enjoin obedience, to make passion yield to reason and individual reason to public reason, something was certainly required which was stronger than physical strength, more deserving of respect than personal interest, more reliable than a philosophical theory, more immutable than a convention, something which was deep in every heart and ruled there.

This thing was belief. Nothing has greater sway over the soul. A belief is the work of our mind, but we are not free to modify it as we choose. It is our creation, but we do not know it. It is human, and we believe it to be divine. . . . It is within us; it never leaves us; it speaks to us at every moment. If it tells us to obey, we obey; if it sets forth our obligations, we comply. Man may subdue his own nature, but he submits to his own thought.

There was an ancient belief which commanded men to honor their ancestors. Ancestor worship gathered the family around an altar. Hence the first religion, the first prayers, the first notion of duty, and the first morality; here property was established, and the order of succession arranged; finally, it was the source of all private law and the regulation of household organization.

Then this belief expanded, and so did the size of the association. As men realized that they had certain divinities in common, they formed wider groups. The same rules worked out and imposed within the family gradually applied to the phratry, the tribe, and the city.

Let us cast an eye over the road men have traveled. In the beginning, the family lived in isolation and man knew only his domestic gods. Above the family, there emerged the phratry with its own god. Lastly, there appeared the city, and men began to think in terms of a god whose providence encompasses the entire city. The hierarchy of associations accompanied the hierarchy of beliefs. Among ancient peoples, the religious idea was the breath which inspired and organized society.

The traditions of the Hindus, the Greeks, and the Etruscans recount that the gods revealed social laws to men. There is a certain truth in this legend. The social laws were the work of the gods; but these gods who were so powerful and so beneficent were nothing but men's own beliefs.

This is how the state came into being among ancient peoples.[1]

Not only does this process assemble all men who depended

---

[1] Fustel de Coulanges, *La Cité antique*, pp. 149–150.

upon the same gods into an enduring "society"; it also gives them a leader:

> Just as in the family authority was inherent in priesthood, and the father, as head of the domestic worship, was both judge and ruler, so the high priest of the city was also its political head. As Aristotle put it, the altar conferred this dignity upon him.

Because there was no adequate constraining machinery when nations were still in their infancy, religion was the only impelling idea vigorous enough to command the obedience of their citizens. But religion did more than incorporate individuals into a solidly constructed society, separated from similar societies by the gap opened by differences in beliefs and enclosed within a potential well to which men of any other faith had no access. Discontinuities between rival societies prevented any confusion. Like the electrons in the atom, men either belong to a society or they do not—though they may belong to several social groups at the same time—and there is no halfway house.

Religion did not merely establish the state and leave it at that, however. By giving the state a head, it created royal power:

> The city religion was involved in everything. At every moment, man was aware that he depended upon his gods, and, consequently, upon the priest who was the intermediary between him and them. This priest guarded the sacred fire; it was he, as Pindar said, whose daily prayers daily saved the city. It was he who knew the formulas of the prayers the gods could not resist; just before a battle, he sacrificed the victim and called down the protection of the gods upon the army. It was altogether natural that a man equipped with such power should be accepted and recognized as leader. Because religion was involved

in government, justice, and war, it necessarily ensued that the priest was at the same time magistrate, judge, and commander in chief. The Kings of Sparta, Aristotle says, have three functions: they perform sacrifices, they wage war, and they dispense justice. Dionysius of Halicarnassus says the same thing about the Kings of Rome.[2]

So it was not strength but religion that first set up kings in ancient cities, as it had the head of the family within its own household.

But these kings, invested with authority by the gods and arrayed with the dignities of priest, prophet, or pontiff, remained men. Essentially, their power was exercised through commands, i.e. by direct action upon individual behavior. By coordinating individual behavior, the royal power successfully assembled collections of physically independent individuals into enduring "societies." The units thus established gradually coalesced into larger and larger groups. Families, *gentes*, tribes, and cities formed the successive levels of organization in human societies. As they expanded, the king used a hierarchy of subordinate chiefs to spread his commands and ensure their observance, passing his own authority on to his representatives.

Nevertheless, the supreme head always retained the mandate he had received by divine investiture. It was what made him "legitimate." The transcendental origin of sovereignty is confirmed by its evolution. In all its future forms, power —replicating the process which had generated it, as does the fetus in the mother's womb—would strive to prove its legitimacy in supernatural terms. The absolute monarchy which ruled over France in the seventeenth century was sanctioned by "divine right." The religious ceremony of the coronation,

[2] Ibid., p. 206.

completed by the anointing with the holy oil, conferred legitimacy upon it. Hereditary descent was considered proof of divine election.

Even the most materialistic governments, such as those in power in the people's republics, base their sovereignties on some transcendental principle. Despite their various modalities, popular elections are, in modern states, the magic fount of sovereignty.

The geographical extension of sovereignties

By controlling individual behavior within his area of sovereignty, the king was able to establish peace among most of his subjects. Because his power stopped at the city's boundaries, however, as soon as neighboring cities were no longer protected by geographic isolation, their interrelationships reverted to the "natural" state—that is, they became warlike and aggressive.

The *amphictyons* did establish a common religion, in the hope that ties of friendship would result from a "sacred meal and a collective libation." But this was merely a confederation. Though war became less frequent, it could not be excluded from the relations between rival cities when there was no centralized governing authority.

Not until the Roman conquest, which destroyed municipal autonomy and established the *imperium Romanum*, was peace brought to the world of the Empire. Only the Roman city remained an independent unit. All the others, stripped of their institutions and law, were subject to the unlimited authority of the leader upon whom Rome had conferred the *imperium*. Thus the *pax Romana* was established, especially during the republican and senatorial regimes. Relying on the totalitarian system that had pacified the city, it was the product of the complete subjection of all the conquered provinces.

The establishment in France of the Capetian monarchy provides an analogous example of pacification through the gradual subjection of feudal sovereignties to a single authority. In the same way, major federations—like the United States or the Soviet Union—successfully impose over wide areas a type of peace which is quite comparable, *mutatis mutandis*, to the *pax Romana*. Their authoritarian action influences the behavior of such aggregate entities as the federated states.

Communities like the United Nations and the European Communities establish an international power, which tends to weaken the natural aggressiveness inherent in relations between states. Again, such organizations confer upon their peoples the benefits of a peace similar to the one achieved by the difficult, and often painful, construction of an efficient sovereignty among the people of a single city or nation.

The secularization of royal power

In the primitive city, the nature of the royal power was undetermined. It bordered on both the divine and the human and, more specifically, on both biological reality and Promethean creation.

Being of a religious nature, it

> had founded the family, then the city; established domestic law and the government of the *gens*, then civil laws and municipal government. Sovereignty derived from religion and was no different from it; kings and magistrates were priests. . . . But the human spirit gradually grew in strength and generated new beliefs. . . . It stopped believing in the old divinities of its infancy, in those dead people who lived in tombs, in those sacred ancestors who must still be given food. It accepted the idea that the gods were no longer the exclusive property of a family or city, but that they watched over the whole universe. . . . Then philosophy appeared and overthrew all the rules

of the old politics. . . . The Sophists substituted for knowledge of the old customs the arts of reasoning and discuss-
ing, dialectic and rhetoric. . . . Plato, like Socrates and
the Sophists, declared that the basis of morality and politics was within ourselves, that tradition was nothing. For
Aristotle, "The law is reason."

Thus, without changing its form, power changed its source.

As government became more difficult and more complicated, as piety was no longer the main requirement,
and skill, prudence, and courage were now necessary,
people no longer believed that the voice of fate was enough
for the selection of a good magistrate. The city no longer
wanted to be bound by the will of the gods; it wanted
to be free to choose its own leaders.[3]

In Attica, the *archon*, who was a priest, was always designated by the gods, while the *strategos*, in whose hands lay
the material interests of the city, was chosen by men. Solon
received the power to legislate from the people. So did the
Decemvirs the mandate to revise the Twelve Tablets, which
provided as follows: "What the will of the people has proclaimed, that is the law."[4] At the same time, the consulate
became less and less of a priesthood and more and more a
secular authority.

Even though forms of government remained unchanged and
Caesar retained his role of supreme pontiff, throughout the
whole ancient world election was no longer the prerogative
of the gods. It proceeded from the consensus of the people.
Popular suffrage replaced divine election, and the will of the
majority became the criterion of legitimacy.

Thus, in the course of the five centuries preceding the advent

[3] Ibid., pp. 415–421, 379.
[4] Livy, VII, 17; IX, 33, 34.

of Christianity, the alliance between religion, on the one hand, and law and politics on the other, was broken. The split between religion and government sprang from the weakening of religion rather than the strengthening of government:

> If society was no longer governed by the old religion, it was because religion was no longer as strong as it had been. But the day came when the religious spirit regained its life and vigor and, in the form of Christianity, belief once more held sway over the human soul. Was the world about to see once more the old confusion of government and priesthood, of faith and law?

At that moment, Christian revelation transformed even the idea of divinity:

> Whereas previously every man had made his own god and there had been as many gods as families and cities, now God appeared as a unique, immense, universal being, the single animator of the universe and the sole object of man's need to worship.

Whereas in the ancient world the state had been governed by the gods, who appointed its leaders through augury or omen, and the state, in its turn, intervened in the realm of conscience and punished every offense against the rites and religion of the city, Jesus Christ taught that His kingdom is not of this world; what is more, He specified: "Render unto Caesar the things that are Caesar's, and unto God the things that are God's." Henceforth, law was to be independent of religion:

> It drew its rules from the human conscience, from the notion of justice which dwells within us all. It could develop at full liberty, reform itself and improve without any obstacle, follow the progress of morality, yield to

the interests and social requirements of succeeding generations.[5]

The division of authority between God and Caesar—with the former continuing to govern the souls while the latter governed the bodies—profoundly changed the roots of order in human societies. Faith, based on divine authority, still derived from traditions whose origin was lost in the dark and distant history of primitive societies. Whether imposed by revelation or inspired, it seemed to be an extension of the biological requirements of life in society. Those demands, like the religious sense in all humankind, were themselves included in man's inheritance. Caesar's decisions, whether he was a monarch, a college, or a parliament, were no more than the expression of his own will. *"Car tel est notre plaisir,"* was the motto of the Kings of France, and, *"Le Roy le veult,"* that of the Kings of England.

Because of the difference in their respective natures, the kings and the gods, in their interventions, relied on different procedures to create respect for their commandments. Royal authority, when it became secularized, did not, of course, relinquish the coercive powers of political ideology. But political ideology, deprived of its transcendental foundation, had to rely upon very human sacred scriptures, such as the Bill of Rights, Marx's, Lenin's, or Mao's writings, and Hitler's *Mein Kampf.* To propagate and conserve faith, authoritarian regimes used parties patterned after the Church: self-criticism replaced confession, and committees for public safety and disciplinary tribunals were substituted for the Inquisition.

But it was mainly because they influenced individual behavior by altogether different processes that the action of the kings was different from that of the Gods. As royal power could depend upon voluntary obedience to a far lesser extent, except when the fate of the motherland was at stake, it had

---

[5] Coulanges, op. cit., pp. 458, 463.

to place considerable emphasis on constraining action. More and more complicated administrative authorities were called upon to implement or enforce decrees.

A police system was entrusted with the task of discovering cases of infringement, and courts were established to pronounce penalties—of a purely earthly sort—that would influence the wills of individuals.

Reward, in the form of honors, titles, and decorations, was then added to constraint. The attractiveness of such recompenses strengthened the efficacy of threatened punishments.

Thus the dichotomy of power between gods and kings did not alter the principle of Promethean intervention. It simply demanded that the now secularized kings offset the loss of control over souls by establishing equally effective control over men's bodies. In each case the purpose was the same: the creation, through control of individual behavior, of the social order wanted by the royal power.

In primitive societies, order is established through the complete and utter subjection of all human beings to the royal will:

> Religion, which had given birth to the State, and the State which supported religion were backstopping each other and in fact were one single entity; these two powers, in an associative coalescence, had almost superhuman strength. . . . Nothing in man was independent. His body belonged to the State and was dedicated to its defense. . . . His wealth was always at the disposal of the State. His private life could not escape this omnipotence. . . . Nor did man have any choice as to what he would believe. Freedom of thought, so far as the state religion was concerned, was unknown. The human person was held of no account by that sacred and almost divine authority which was called the *patria* or the State.[6]

[6] Ibid., pp. 265–268.

At the time when the government of ancient societies lost its purely religious foundations, its omnipotence remained entire, whether it was a monarchy, an aristocracy, or a democracy. Man, bereft of liberty, was reduced to subservience in his soul and body. Power was really all-embracing, and the regime was a totalitarian one.

The decentralization of royal power

Gradually, however, the efforts of the oppressed classes, the overthrow of the priestly caste, the work of the philosophers, and the progress of human thought shattered the old principles of human association. Since it was consubstantial with religion—that is, with man's opinion of the divinity—the status of the human person was bound to evolve as well. This evolution was realized by the theory of "right."

Right is a certain freedom of decision that subjects behavior, within the province to which it applies, to the will of the individual alone. Thus, sovereignty, within that area, is transferred from the pontiff or chief in which it had been vested to the person to whom that right has been granted. By restoring to that individual control of his actions, this effects a genuine decentralization of power.

In Western civilization, the history of Roman law illustrates this process. The rules that it laid down affected the status of individuals, of relations between individuals, and of relationships between individuals and the things they desired, which were called wealth.

In terms of the status of individuals, the first decentralization transferred the power of the religious leader of a tribe or *gens* to a limited number of persons. These were marked by three characteristics:

the *status libertatis,* under which they were free beings, and not slaves;

the *status civitatis,* under which they were Roman citizens
and not Latins or aliens;

the *status familiae,* under which they were heads of families and not beings *in potestate.*

These three attributes, which formed the legal personality,
conferred upon their beneficiaries, who were called Roman
citizens, and upon them alone, the freedoms of action set
forth by the law. In particular, the law granted them freedom
of the city, the right to vote, the right to be elected to the
magistracy, the right to serve in the legions, the right to marry
and establish a Roman family under the unlimited authority
of the *paterfamilias,* the right to own property and to enter
into contracts and to use to that end the guarantees provided
by the Roman civil law, and the right to legal proceedings.

The Latins, on the other hand, did not enjoy the privileges
of legal personality. They were divided into three classes whose
rights increased according to the antiquity of their status as
Latins. The aliens came under the laws of their cities and
the law of nations, but only to the extent that Rome granted
them that privilege. The slaves, for their part, had no rights
at all. Regarded as objects, they belonged unreservedly to
their masters, whose will replaced theirs.

Thus, under the earlier Roman law a limited number of
human beings were granted the freedoms of choice provided
for by the law. Gradually, the number of such persons increased, until it included virtually all human beings after the
abolition of slavery and serfdom, though that was not complete.

The content of the rights—i.e. the total number of liberties
which might not be violated—gradually developed and continues to expand in our day. For example, man won the right
to think—which religious authority, and especially the Inquisition, had denied him, as the civil power was eventually
to do in totalitarian states. Other rights include free speech

and press and freedom to move from one place to another, to marry, to leave paternal authority. Married women were granted the rights to gainful employment, to keep their earnings, to enter into contracts, and to own property.

The rights to think, to move from one place to another, and to practice a trade do not imply any obligation to think, to move, or to work professionally. They simply grant the liberty to choose freely what one will think, where one will move, what activity one will carry out. Like all others, these rights simply define an area of free choice in which the behavior of the individual will be what he wants it to be; within that area he can generate structures and himself exercise the lofty role of a "creator."

Most of the rights we have listed have to do with relations between or among individuals. The so-called property rights, which regulate the relations between individuals and the desired things known as wealth, deserve closer analysis. In Rome, the right to property was not an attribute of the human person. The only individual who enjoyed it was the *paterfamilias*, a person completely independent from anybody else. Only with "the declaration of the rights of man and the citizen" did property rights become an inherent characteristic of the human person. After a long evolution, they were defined. In France, for example, Article 544 of the Civil Code lists "the right to enjoy and dispose of things absolutely, provided no one makes use of them in a way prohibited by law or by implementing regulations." This definition of property rights in no way specifies the way a property owner is to use or dispose of his possessions. It leaves him entirely free to act as he wishes in regard to them, subject to the provisions of the relevant laws and regulations. Thus, within these limits, the thing owned is controlled by its owner and by him alone, as a machine is controlled by its operator.

Of course, despite property rights, the government may exercise authority over a possession according to the provisions of the laws and regulations. Apart from those, however, the individual owner enjoys full sovereignty over his property. To understand the full implications of this, take the example of the landowner. It is his choice whether the land will produce wheat, oats, or rapeseed. I shall never forget the pride of one of my neighbors when he was handicapped by illness. He refused to let his grandchildren see him because he wanted them to remember him, in his words, "as the landlord towering above his pastures." Could there be a more conscious expression of the feeling of sovereignty? In everything that concerns its cultivation, a landowner is truly king of his property.

The evolution of right moved in a uniform and remarkably continuous way. In the beginning, all rights belonged to the head of the *gens* or the tribe, who was simultaneously god and king, and other creatures had absolutely no freedom of decision. Ultimately, full rights, i.e. virtually unlimited sovereignty, were granted to all human beings, subject to the limitations laid down by laws or regulations.

The hierarchy of the Promethean "creators"

The Promethean universe exists and is developing around us every day. We have certain knowledge, at least as regards its contemporary progress, that it is the result of a "creation" whose authors we recognize. This creation never originates from a *tabula rasa*, but is always the outcome of a modification of preexisting structures. It is these structures that are "ordered"; that is to say, they are submitted to the requirements of the creating thought. Modification of these structures is always effected by machines, and those machines, no matter how automated they may be, are ultimately controlled by persons. It is these persons, the generators of the Promethean order, that we shall now try to identify.

In primitive social groups—generally based on the family—the Promethean order arose from the transformation of structures that were apparently included in man's biological inheritance; they were therefore generated by instinct rather than reason. Such societies are essentially authoritarian. The power of the leader who was both king and priest was founded on religious ideology and on the means of constraint granted him not only by his own strength but by that of those people whose assistance he obtained as a result of his consecration. At this stage, it was the will of the leader, as revealed or inspired by the divinity whose emanation he is, that generated social structures. He was, directly or indirectly, "creator."

The granting of rights to certain individuals, however, truly dismembered the royal prerogative. For example, the rights to think, to write, to study, enabled their holders to produce poems or symphonies, or to invent wave mechanics. Similarly, by freely choosing his own activity, a farmer creates the harvest of his fields, the craftsman the product of the shop where he works, the industrialist the output of the factory he runs. All of them, by reason of the liberty conferred upon them by the rights they hold, are endowed with the power to create within the areas defined by those rights.

A property owner in particular has this creative power with respect to his own possessions. Secure in the right to use or even abuse his wealth, on the sole condition that he does not violate the laws or regulations, he truly controls whatever he owns. By transforming his property, by combining it with other things, by putting energy into it, he creates new structures. In this way he constantly directs the evolution of the Promethean order in our universe. The rational property owner plans his action to ensure that it fulfills his desires to the greatest extent possible.

Ownership, however, encompasses not only the right to own a thing, but also freedom to dispose of it. We have already seen that, as soon as it came into existence, this right inevitably generated trade and, therefore, the market. In the market, the price mechanism granted each individual with some purchasing power the ability to determine, according to his own desires, the structure of the productive apparatus, even that outside the realm of his own possessions, depending on the way he chose to use it.

Organizational power, which in totalitarian systems is entirely in the hands of the planning authority, thus passed into the hands of the demanding parties in the market. Each such party, whether an individual or a collective entity, imposed a pattern of his own choice upon that fraction of the productive apparatus commensurate with the size of his own demand relative to aggregate demand. The royal prerogative, which had generated order, was thus distributed among all those who had power to determine, through their respective demands, the structure of a corresponding portion of the entire surrounding economic space.

Thus it was that the complex hierarchy of sovereignties making up Promethean power in the world of men gradually took shape. Originally, there was one single authority—that of the priest-king, who held his power from the ideology he represented on earth and from the constraining influences that accompanied it. In his dual capacity as enforcer and interpreter of the divine word, he controlled individual behavior and, by determining it, shaped social structures. The split of the royal power between God and Caesar left the priest-king with sway over souls but granted the temporal ruler power over men's bodies.

The rise of the human person dismembered temporal power by forcing it to grant, first to a certain number of privileged persons and later to every individual and aggregate entity, the prerogatives of free determination called "rights."

Within each of these rights—to some extent limited by the dictates of his religion, his moral code, or the laws and regulations to which he was subject—the individual (or the corporate body or entity) came to plan his own activity freely.

The most widespread of these rights, those of property, grant the individual royal power over everything he possesses. The freedom of disposition extends this power over owned objects to everything which can be acquired through trade. Hence the sovereignty derived from property rights is not limited to the substance of things actually possessed. Through the property holder's discretionary decision making, this sovereignty can be transferred—provided an appropriate trade takes place—to any other part of the universe having the same value as that which has been relinquished. The property holder thus rules over a realm with undetermined frontiers, whose extent is established by the value of the goods he possesses. He can further increase the area of his sovereignty to the extent that lenders agree to relinquish and transfer to him the prerogatives of free choice attached to the capital loaned.

Whether he is a director of a nationalized firm, the head of an industrial, agricultural, or craft undertaking, or a free man who controls nothing but his own body and, possibly, the goods belonging to him, these sovereign prerogatives make such a man an all-powerful king within the realm of his possessions. His power is subject only to limitations imposed upon him by his God, his morality, and the secular laws and regulations enacted by the societies of which he is a member.

More specifically, such royal power is the prerogative of the head of a family who, subject to the same restrictions, directs the family group as he wishes. Cognizant of the resources he commands and of the abilities of each of his "subjects," he not only directs exchanges with the external world but also, by his totalitarian authority, determines a fair distribution of work and profits inside the group. For this reason, families, as the lowest stratum of human societies, are basically many small communistic cells; they constitute the molecules of social structures.

Thus, again, the hierarchy of royal powers reveals the chain of social structures. Starting with the quantum of existence represented by the individual, and with the family molecule and intermediate political, economic, or social communities in between, it culminates in those enormous communal societies which may usher in a single community of men in a not too distant future. It is the hierarchy of all these royal powers as a whole that has shaped and continues to shape in our day the Promethean order of human societies.

CHAPTER XI

The Gods

*The major problem: order in the
non-Promethean universe*

THE PROMETHEAN UNIVERSE is the expression of a certain arrangement of its constituent elements; in other words, it is the materialization of one order from among all the orders possible.

This order, which is complex and therefore highly improbably, is never spontaneous. We are certain that it is inevitably the expression of a thought: it has been established by kings who rule over their respective domains and who, within those domains, wield the scepter of constraining action. The causes of the various aspects of the Promethean order can be easily identified, because they can always be traced to an individual or an entity able and willing to bring it about, with the help of the machines under his command. Thus, the Promethean order is always the product of the will of a "creator."

Below the Promethean universe, however, there are orders which are no less complex: those which constitute "nature." These range from the atom, if not from more fundamental particles, up to and including man, and they encompass all the societies of the inanimate and animate universe.

These orders too, in their complexity, are infinitely improbable. Like Promethean orders, they are the products of "machines" capable of producing them, such as the atom or the molecule, chlorophyll or the ovum. But these machines are not thought of, willed by, or made by men. Nevertheless, they exist.

Faced with the enormous amount of order that the universe represents, all of it so highly improbable, the human intelligence, characterized by the principle of sufficient reason ("Every effect must have a cause") which seems to be one of its innate characteristics, demanded an explanation. It found several, and they can be divided into two quite distinct groups. These will be the topic of this closing chapter.

The two alternatives: a divine institution
or chance plus natural selection

Explanation is one of the requirements of the human mind. But if any explanation is to be accepted, it must satisfy all the dominant ideas of the mind in any particular epoch. Certain of these ideas seem so innate that all of us still share them: reverence for father and mother, respect for ancestors, belief in their survival, invocation of their protection.

Burial ceremonies, the tending of graves and tombs, the inscription of names on tombstones, the placing of flowers on the resting-places on the anniversaries of death, can be explained only by a deep, ingrained and spontaneous belief in survival after death. This belief transformed the dead individual into a sacred being, to whom prayers were addressed and whose benevolence was solicited by sacrifice.

If each of us investigates his inmost conscience, he will find that there is still that same reverence for one's begetter, that same care to emulate and obey him. Ancestor worship has existed in all places and at all times. Its universality and the survival of its forms, even where people are most reluctant to admit its principle, lead us to believe that it is an innate characteristic of human nature, both biological and psychological.

I do not intend to write the history of religious feeling here. I shall simply note that the gradual refinement of the religion of the begetting ancestor, the object of the prayers of his descendants, was to lead to the notion of the gods of the city, from whose hands every town expected its salvation: "Gods of this city, do not allow it to be destroyed with our houses and our hearths."[1] The same faith spread and blossomed into the cult of the protecting divinity which, in its omnipotence, created that part of the universe for which it assumed responsibility.

Judaism and Christianity removed the divinity from the world of men and established it outside and above visible nature.

> Whereas previously every man had created his own god and there were as many gods as families and cities, now God appeared as a unique being, immense, universal, the single animator of the universe and the sole object of man's need to worship. . . . Man no longer gave God food and drink: prayer was no longer a formula of incantation; it was an act of faith and humble request; fear of the gods had been replaced by love of God.[2]

> The natural course of things is not something which, as Father Wilhelm Schmidt puts it, is self-explanatory to men, but something which man does not understand until and unless he has made it intelligible to himself. . . . No matter where we find him, man was able to form universal ideas, to condense a multitude of things into a group and all the groups into a single notion of the whole universe; he searched for their creator and, applying

---

[1] Aeschylus, *Seven Against Thebes.*
[2] Fustel de Coulanges, *La Cité antique,* pp. 458–459.

the principle of causality he had come to master, reached the point where he discovered this creator through rational judgement. . . . Claude Lévi-Strauss says that so-called primitive peoples devised a reasonable way of fitting irrationality, in its double aspect of logical contingency and affective turbulence, into rationality.[3]

Thus the threshold of history appears in the first lines of the book of Genesis: "In the beginning God created the heaven and the earth."

The same formula conquered the Christian West with, "I believe in God, the Father almighty, maker of heaven and earth." St. Thomas Aquinas cast further light on the concept of creation by stating that "it behooves Divine Providence to conserve order in the world."[4] Descartes argued that "we know with great certainty that God preordained all things, and what we know of God assures us that His power is so great that it would be a crime to think we could ever be capable of doing anything he had not previously ordained."[5]

Thus, there is order in the universe only because such order was conceived and willed by its Creator—as were all Promethean orders, which are the products of human thought and will. The difference between the former and the latter does not lie in their cause, therefore, but in the nature of the means whose outcome they are. The means are natural as regards the latter, because they result from the knowledge which certain men have derived from the nature of things. The means are supernatural as regards the former, because they proceed from the mysterious efficacy of an absolute and immediate power over the whole universe.

Progress in scientific knowledge, however, raised more and more pressing objections against the thesis of creation as an

[3] Robert Aron, *Dieu des origines*, 1966, pp. 27–29.
[4] *Summa Contra Gentes*, III, lxxviii.
[5] *Principia Philosophiae*, 40.

immediately efficacious act of will of one or more omnipotent creators. Nevertheless, man could not evade his fundamental requirement: the need to understand. He no longer understood because he no longer accepted the transcendental explanation *in toto*.

To avoid disappointing man and to provide, despite the progress of knowledge, the explanation he required, some scientific minds have elaborated another system of explanation, one which seemed to them more compatible with the teachings of science. This views creation as the gradual occupancy of all possibilities as a result of fortuitous encounters; natural selection assures the survival and multiplication of the solutions that preserve existence and the elimination of those that work against it.

This complicated and subtle thesis has been put forth by several writers, who consider it the antidote to the religious explanation. In order not to betray the ideas of its proponents, I shall simply reprint the exposition of one of the most brilliant of them, Pierre Auger:

> If the number of independent elements in a system increases, the chances that those elements will transiently realize an ordered system decrease.
>
> Conversely, if a system includes a small number of elements, it has a greater chance of passing through ordered states during the course of time. . . . What we are talking about here is a fluctuation of order just like those fluctuations of density and temperature that occur as soon as the volume of matter under consideration is small enough to include only a few distinct elements.
>
> Under ordinary conditions, these fluctuations fortuitously appear and disappear at every instant. But if a fluctuation generates an arrangement that is permanent or seems at least temporarily stable, and if the resultant microscopic grouping is capable of catalytic action which

will trigger off a certain transformation of the medium, then its effects are increased. . . . We can understand the important role fluctuations can play when special conditions allow them to act as catalyst in massive transformations: they leave their mark on huge groupings of molecules, even though they are fundamentally a part of events which encompass only a small number of elements. Thus the consequences of characteristic phenomena of the microscopic world are amplified and reach a macroscopic scale. . . .

An elementary creation cannot, however, extend itself as the result of a mere amplification. If the edifice that has been begun is to develop, new creations must be added to the initial, necessarily simple structure, which must grow in complexity. Such developments need not call new machinery into play; progress through successive stages of fixed fluctuations on an increased scale is enough. . . .

Consider, for example, the construction of a very complex molecule involving the combination of several elements present in the medium. As soon as more than two elements must be combined, the operation, viewed as a single act, represents a fluctuation which is so improbable that it would ordinarily require a very long time to happen. But if a combination of two of the necessary elements can occur of itself in the first stage, so that the chance arrival of subsequent elements can be anticipated, the probability is increased to more acceptable levels.

If the proposed structure requires that an even greater number of constituents be placed in very precise positions in relation to one another, the formation of the final complex in a single act has an almost nonexistent probability which would take thousands of years to materialize. On the other hand, the structure may grow without recourse to miracles if the process occurs in stages, with successively incomplete complexes attaining at least temporary stability. In each stage, the partial complex waits for chance to bring it its next element. If it cannot wait and collapses too quickly, or if it is unable to grasp an opportunity, the final complex remains in the vast limbo of possibilities that will never materialize.

This analysis divides creation into a sequence of successive stages, each based on initial permanence and a favorable medium that can "wait" without deteriorating. Then, after an indeterminate period, a fluctuation occurs which adds a new element and is in fact the beginning of a new permanence. If this stage endures—if, that is, it expands, and reproduces itself so that it can resist evolution toward disorder—it becomes the basis for new stages which will appear during the course of time. . . .

Waiting, fluctuation, amplification—these are the essentials of this process, during which nothing happens that bears the slightest resemblance to tendency toward a fixed goal.[6]

Nevertheless, the theory of fortuitous creation cannot of itself solve the great problem of organic adaptation. It does not explain the highly improbable harmonies revealed by the universe, especially the universe of living beings. These harmonies are extremely imperfect, of course, but sufficient to suggest the idea of a design, an intention, a finality.

Lamarckian theory gives a reason for this finality—"a naive reason, certainly, but a reason indeed, since it postulates directly adaptive variations."[7] If one accepts the thesis that chance fluctuations represent the prime mover of evolution, they seem to be nothing more than pure germinal accidents,

[6] Pierre Auger, *L'homme microscopique*, 1952, pp. 38ff.
[7] Jean Rostand, *Ce que je crois*, p. 31.

with no utilitarian value whatsoever. Essentially indifferent or neutral, they cannot fit into the progressive current that characterizes the orthogenesis of the universe.

In order to explain the continuity of progress, proponents of the chance theory have supplemented it with declarations that mutations have been screened out by natural selection throughout the ages. In their view, any change unfavorable to existence was eliminated, so that only favorable changes subsisted. These, in combination with one another, provide an explanation for the continuing progress which is characteristic of the evolution of our universe, especially of the living species.

What I know and what I believe

Having reached the end of this book, I am obliged, in courtesy to those who have done me the honor of reading it, to inform them of what I believe I know. Similarly, I cannot conceal what, with much hesitation and uncertainty, I know I believe.

My knowledge is essentially concerned with the resemblances between the orders of nature, whose final ends we do not know (nor even whether they have any), and the orders established by certain men, which we know to have been willed, conceived, and realized by them. The main purpose of the preceding pages has been to cast light on these similarities and to convince my readers of their reality.

My beliefs relate to the lessons I have drawn from these similarities. It is difficult to formulate such lessons because they are so imprecise. Let me hasten to add that they are a matter of faith rather than of scientific knowledge, that they are part of that intimate stock of inclinations one hardly dares bring to full light, and that they are of value only to those who have worked them out on the basis of their own experience and for their own use.

The Gods and the Kings

I know, first of all, that the orders willed by men have the same structure as the orders created by nature. They are always social orders and, as such, are the outcome of the integration into a lasting society of individuals belonging to a lower level of organization. Thus our universe is a vast combination of quanta of existence. Each particle is a society for individuals of the next lower rank and an individual for the societies of the next higher level.

Every society is produced by highly varied interactions among its members. It is established as soon as these actions become sufficiently intense to enclose and retain the individuals they affect within one potential well.

Interactions become efficacious either through the juxtaposition of the individuals involved or through addition of energy. The latter makes it possible for individuals to leap over the rim of a preexisting potential well or across the threshold of private life, each of which protects the quanta of existence in its own sphere. Interaction between two individuals, though a generally acknowledged fact, is nearly always mysterious, especially in its "emergence" of the particles involved. Interpretation in terms of "fields"—such as a force field, an electrical field, a magnetic field, or fields of sexual attraction, love, or hate—may verify the fact of interaction but does not afford an explanation of it.

The order of our universe is the result of the gradual complication of preexisting orders, a complication which is effected by the addition of individuals or energy. Hence it cannot be accomplished except in terms of societies of the next lower rank to the one the new entity will occupy in the hierarchy of organizational levels.

Thus creation can only be the result of an evolution. It is contingent but irreversible to the extent that, on each level of existence, it results from a decisive shift of direction. Each such shift is itself contingent, but once it is finally accomplished, it determines the bases on which new orders will be constructed.

Creation is never immediate. It is always effected through monitoring control systems, called "machines." These impart to the interactions generating the social order an efficacy that will make it a reality. The *Fiat lux* phenomenon has never been observed, and could arise only in connection with the fundamental particles of the universe, if there.

These characteristics are common to all societies that make up a "creation," whether it is "Promethean," i.e. the product of man's will, or "natural." The major difference between the two types of societies is that we know the creators of the first type—the human societies or those of inanimate particles, i.e. man-made objects. We have certain knowledge that they have been conceived, willed, and realized by men. We realize that **they** are the embodiment of a thought whose author or authors can be identified. We can identify and name the men who have extracted them from the vast range of possibilities precisely so that they could be endowed with reality.

On the other hand, we have found that the societies that make up nature simply exist. We can gauge their extreme improbability, but we have never achieved direct cognizance of the idea which may have generated them and whose materialization they are. We do not know whether there is such an idea, whether these societies have any finality, or, if they have, what it is. We can never objectively identify a will to which they would owe their existence.

In the presence of these natural orders—which I have called Jupiterian to distinguish them from Promethean orders and to show their anteriority—we encounter the two lines of explanation mentioned earlier. The first of these, which is older and more widely accepted, is the religious explanation. It takes many and various forms, but it always views "creation" as the deliberate and conscious act of one or more all-powerful deities.

I shall not enter into a discussion of the historicity of the revelations "Creators" are said to have resorted to in order to make their existence and their will known to men. The problem of historical authenticity cannot, in any case, be divorced from the possibility of the inspiration: one or several gods have been said to have caused, by supernatural means, certain men—their prophets—to decide to reveal to other men the existence and teachings of the God who had created them.

On the other hand, I recognize that as knowledge has advanced, the explanation of creation by an act of free will of one or several almighty creators has become less and less acceptable to growing numbers of people. The permanence of the laws of nature has increasingly struck them as incompatible with the contingency and liberty of the act of creation.

Similarly, the widespread phenomenon of creation by machines—self-reproductive molecules, chlorophyll, the ovum—has led men increasingly away from belief in the immediate and creative power of the Word. Finally, the discovery of the principle of evolution, its widespread application, and its necessarily progressive character are obstacles to explanations of creation in terms of the act of discretionary will manifested in the divine *Fiat lux*.

But explanation by chance plus natural selection also raises serious objections. First of all, the likelihood that successive fluctuations could explain the entire evolution of our universe seems to me extremely slight. I cannot accept the view that the immensely complicated and perfectly rational creations which our universe, especially the living world, reveals are the effect of chance encounters, even though they may have been prepared for billions of years. Can anyone imagine that the location of the eye in living species is the result of pure chance, stemming from the elimination, through vital competition, of species which may have had their eyes in their backs or in the soles of their feet? Can anyone imagine that the spread through many species of the proven solutions to the problems of locomotion, respiration, digestion—all of which are so clearly oriented toward the maintenance and conservation of life—are fortuitous phenomena? Can anyone imagine that some of the prodigious phenomena of reproduction—such as the meiosis and mitosis of a fertilized ovum, a subtle mechanism splendidly adapted to the transmission of parental characteristics—are the product of chance?

Nor would an explanation concerning only spatial or temporal characteristics of the encounters which have generated these complex groupings be sufficient. To be fruitful, they must have been endowed with conditions of energy that are highly improbable themselves; yet without these the new society could never have come into being.

Furthermore, if an order is to subsist once it has materialized, it must not only be stable, but also be immediately reproduced in a sufficient number of copies. Without such replication, it would quickly be destroyed by the hazards of existence, which would sweep it along the powerful current of increasing entropy to the vast cemetery of bygone orders.

It is true that the commandment to increase and multiply is obeyed largely by living species. But increase and multiplication are by no means spontaneous phenomena. They can result only from complex catalytic processes, which, because of the further uncertainty they introduce, make even more improbable any spontaneous ordering of the universe.

Even if one accepted all the unlikely assumptions upon which the theory of fortuitous creation rests, however, the need for a final cause would not be truly eliminated. If an order which had materialized by chance was to subsist, it would have to be established and maintained by adequate interactions. And those could only result from the very nature of the particles involved.

Furthermore, the progressive rise of order in the universe

implies that, on each level of organization, the embodiment of a possibility brought about the emergence of new interactions. These, in turn, generated, on the next higher level, new ranges of possibilities, themselves fully determined. Thus, all the possibilities in our universe would have to be implicit in the original particles, as an animal's characteristics are in the sex cells which generated it. This would bring us back to the theory of total predetermination. The explanation would be no different from Laplace's well-known formula, except that it would apply not simply to one path, but to a series of possible paths.

So, even assuming that the culling of order was effected by chance, the idea that final causes have been excluded remains an illusion. Reality can be what it is only if the possibilities from among which it has been culled are what they are. In the last analysis, it must be the characteristics of the fundamental particles—perhaps only of the ultimate particles of energy, if there are any—that established the limits of the valley along which creation dug its bed.

In this strongly paradoxical roundabout way, the theory of creation as the outcome of fortuitous fluctuations joins the spiritualist and religious tradition, since it leads to the admission that "the creation of the universe, the creation of life, the creation of man—all were effected as a unique act, an initial fillip implying all these eventual creations . . . which were included in the one sentence, 'Let there be light.' "[8]

WHAT I BELIEVE

The two rival cosmogonies—of God and of chance—differ from each another because of the nature of the processes they consider responsible for the evolution of the universe. The first generalizes the mechanism of Promethean creation, of

---

[8] Albert Ducrocq, *Logique de la vie*, p. 224.

234

which we have full and direct knowledge through introspection. In the will of one or more almighty creators—acting directly on the quanta of existence composing the universe—it sees the power responsible for its evolution. The second looks for the same secret in coincidental combinations screened out by natural selection.

I myself do not believe that there are such clearcut differences between the two evolutionary processes, one affecting nature and the other human creation.

Compare, for example, the evolution of two specific families: in nature, the equidae, and in the Promethean universe, the "automobilidae." Both these evolved from mutations of the genes in the former case, and of "ideas" in the latter. Both genes and ideas were the vehicles of the inherited patrimony of the species. The success and expansion of the number of individuals in both families—i.e. horses and automobiles—is attributable to the progress that resulted from the mobility of the existents because of these evolutionary mutations.

In each case, however, natural selection directed and oriented the evolution of the species. Think, for example, of the many types of automobiles which were eliminated each year by competition in annual motor shows or on the roads of the world. Clearly, the idea from which Promethean creations derive does not exclude the testing ground of vital competition. The gods prove to be just as humble as men in that they try all possible formulas and blindly submit to the rigors of natural selection.

On the other hand, there are two profound differences between what we can observe of creation in nature and what we know of Promethean creation. In the latter we have certain knowledge of the generating idea behind a created object. We can identify the mind in which the idea originated, we know its end as well as the means, and, in particular, we know the machines that were used to create the object.

In observing creation in nature, on the other hand, we can

never perceive the generating idea directly. In fact, we cannot even assert, objectively, that there is one. To obviate our ignorance of the means by which it was effected, we must fall back upon the hypothesis—so difficult to admit in terms of common sense—that chance mutations were screened out by natural selection.

Thus the explanation of Promethean creation would appear to be simple, clear, and final, while the explanation of the creation for which men have no responsibility is obscure and always uncertain. The former falls within the province of physics, the latter within the province of metaphysics.

This oversimplified opposition is illusory, however, and results from an inadequate analysis of the mechanics of Promethean creation. It appears simple only because it is so familiar that we are unaware of the difficult problems it raises. Like divine creation, Promethean creation is never immediate. It is always produced by machines, which are always the products of other machines, and so on, back to the initial creative action of a body impelled by an idea.

No human machine, and therefore no Promethean creation, would exist if man did not have available to incarnate his ideas the primary machine he calls his body—and especially the hand, the instrument of his body. But the creative acts of our bodies are the outcomes of the movements those bodies perform. These movements result from muscular contractions, which are the effect of nervous stimuli or transfers of hormones, themselves produced by movements of electrons, atoms, ions, or molecules.

If, therefore, our gestures and movements are directed by the thoughts of the person we are, it is because these thoughts are able to stimulate motion in certain particles. How does the transition occur from the timelessness of thought to the spatial-temporal frame in which particles move? We have no idea. And yet our thoughts do command motions in the universe of matter. That is the most mysterious, the most "supernatural," phenomenon in nature.

236

The great scientist and Nobel prize laureate in physics, Erwin Schrödinger, came up against this problem. He began by laying down two premises:

1. My body operates like a perfect machine in accordance with the laws of Nature;

2. Yet, I know, by direct and incontrovertible experience, that I direct its movements, and that I foresee their effects; I know also that these can be momentous, in which case I accept entire responsibility for them.

The only possible inference from these two facts is that it is myself—this "myself" taken in the broadest sense of the word, the meaning which is familiar to any mind aware of its own existence—that is the person, if any, who controls the "movement of atoms" in accordance with the laws of Nature. . . . Then, it would be rash to summarize the factual situation with the simple phrase it calls for: "I am, therefore, God."[9]

If we disregard—as Schrödinger asks us to—what he calls the "blasphemous and insane" nature of this statement, we can see that it leads to this major finding about the problem: thought influences matter.

Even if we discovered the instrumentalities of this action—such as electrical, magnetic, or other fields—its scope would still be of the same magnitude. At best we can establish that thought can be introduced into the spatial-temporal fields which affect the movement of particles; we should by no means have explained how it externalizes itself into a universe which is not its own. Thus there is no escaping this objective conclusion: using the body it commands as an intermediary, human thought exercises a creative power whose nature is entirely unknown to us. This finding brings us back to the great problem often mentioned in previous chapters: the role of psychism in creation.

[9] *Qu'est-ce que la vie?* 1951, p. 150.

We know that creation is effected through the coordination of individual behavior. Coordination causes individuals to enter into a society: by "creating" a society on the next level above that to which the constituent individuals belonged, it establishes a new tier of "creation."

But behavior is the expression of psychism. In the words of my illustrious colleague Jean Rostand: no matter what idea one may have of psychism, it is an essential and ubiquitous biological reality. Consciousness—the mind, if you like—is not the prerogative of the nerve cells; it exists potentially or larvally in every cell of every organism; it underlies every manifestation of life. And in the presence of the vast problem of evolution it might not be unwise to call on all the aspects of life to provide an explanation."[10]

I go further than Rostand and believe that every quantum of existence, because it is an individual, has a behavior, that this behavior is a certain manner of being in the world, a mode of existing. It is the expression of the individual's own nature and, as such, has all the characteristics of psychism, no matter how rudimentary it may seem.

We know nothing about this psychism. However, it leads us to the borders of a vast area, some of whose outcroppings are perceptible—especially those that consciousness reveals to us—but whose deepest nature remains unknown. This is the realm of thought, the foundation of the human person.

Like Jean Rostand, I am convinced that "there is, more or less, only one difference between us and animals, a difference of quantity; we are made of the same stuff, the same substance, as animals."[11] Generalizing from this finding, I believe that if behavior has a cause, it manifests, no matter where it exists, dispositions of varying degrees of complexity but also of a certain degree of permanence over time. These

[10] Rostand, op. cit., p. 40.
[11] Ibid., p. 19.

resemble psychism in their nature. I am not, of course, saying that electrons and protons are capable of the ideas which stimulate love. At most, I am prepared to admit that they have characteristics more or less similar to those responsible for the existence, between male and female, of the attraction which generates the family molecule.

We know nothing about the nature of psychism. Identifying and measuring the nervous and hormonal influxes which underlie the sexual act will never explain love to anyone who has never experienced it. The most painstaking elec-troencephalogram of an ecstatic mystic will never reveal the true nature of his feeling of adoration and communion, of which his consciousness gives him immediate and direct aware-ness. There is, then, no escaping the admission that psychism is a set of faculties of which we are aware only because we can sense their existence within ourselves.

We infer the existence of mind in our fellow beings from the similarity between their behavior and ours, assuming that analogous effects must have analogous causes. But we never perceive these causes. Another person is a universe which remains impenetrable to us. Its internal drama is never fully externalized; it is manifested indirectly by the oral reports of the individual, who is at one and the same time both the stage and the audience, or directly by the actions which it prompts him to perform.

When behavior is in some degree different from ours, we cannot know anything about the mental state it expresses. My poodle is a deep mystery to me. His behavior is of course less complex than ours, but often quite subtle. Knowing what I know about the way my own acts are determined, I cannot help seeing some of my dog's actions as outcroppings into the external world of some sort of a stream of thought. Similarly, a spermatozoon under a microscope or an amoeba under an electron microscope "behaves." Unless we admit the existence of an effect without a cause, we must suppose that they have their own particular natures—that is, that psychism generates the actions they perform in response to messages from the world outside them.

But the self-reproductive DNA molecule, the radioactive atom, the electron, and the proton all have very permanent manners of existing, of being in the world, of behaving in relation to the surrounding media and circumstances. Although we do not know how their reactions are determined, we do know that they are brought about within a precise field of possibilities. In other words, we know that all these actors also display specific behavior. This implies that they have specific natures of their own, with all the characteristics of psychism.

Of all these forms of psychism, we know only our own and, to a certain degree, that of our fellow men. Science studies their external manifestations but has never, to this day, been able to apprehend their true nature and source.

Will it ever be able to?

What we know, of course, is merely the tiniest part of what is knowable. As Louis de Broglie observes:

> For several years now, our knowledge of the number, properties, and forms of particles has grown without interruption in an extraordinary manner. If the ideas we have outlined are correct, every particle and the wave carrying it will emerge, we might say, in the observable microphysical world, into the "surface" of the subquantum medium, a vast reservoir of hidden energy. The evolution and interactions of observable particles, their possible transformations into one another, the appearance and disappearance of photons—perhaps one day all that will strike us as the result of the enormous possibilities lying hidden in the subquantum medium.[12]

[12] Louis de Broglie, *Certitudes et incertitudes de la science*, 1966, p. 65.

Can it be that this universal psychism has its source in that sea which no human eye has yet penetrated to its depths? Will we find there the explanation of that mysterious presence before which our entire existence, and perhaps all the other existences in the universe, unfolds? Is it a single and unique presence, as the Upanishads claim? Or is it divided into immortal souls as numerous as the bodies they enliven.

Given our present state of knowledge, I do not see how we could draw an explanation of the indivisible entity making up the human person from the subquantum medium or from any other objective reality.

My feeling—and I do not say my opinion, since I am aware that it is belief and not scientific knowledge—is summed up in Sir James Jeans's parable of the two-dimensional worms:

It is conceivable that happenings entirely outside the space-time continuum determine what we describe as the "course of events" inside the continuum, and that the apparent indeterminacy of nature may arise merely from our trying to force happenings which occur in many dimensions into a smaller number of dimensions. Imagine, for instance, a race of blind worms, whose perceptions were limited to the two-dimensional surface of the earth. Now and then spots of the earth would become sporadically wet. We, whose faculties range through three dimensions of space, call the phenomenon a rain-shower, and know that events in the third dimension of space determine, absolutely and uniquely, which spots shall become wet and which shall remain dry. But if the worms, unconscious even of the existence of the third dimension of space, tried to thrust all nature into their two-dimensional framework, they would be unable to discover any determinism in the distribution of wet and dry spots; the worm-scientists would only be able to discuss the wetness and dryness of minute areas in terms of probabilities, which they would be tempted to treat as ultimate truth.[13]

Like the blind worms, we can discuss events affected by individual behavior—such as the eventual death of a child who has just been born or the location of a particle in space—only in terms of probability. Theories provide us with the formulas that constitute our science, and then all of us regard them as ultimate truths.

For my part, I regard these ultimate truths as the projection of realities which until now have escaped us. I even think that they will always escape us, and that, though we may know the Promethean creator, it will always be impossible and forbidden to us to construct images of God the maker of heaven and earth. We shall remain blindfolded before Him, because we lack the instruments to see Him. But I see no reason not to attribute the explanation of order in Nature to a universal psychism—whether it be one or manifold.

Thus, despite appearances, the problem of the kings is no less complex and no more accessible than the problem of the gods. In bringing them together in this book, I have attempted to cast some light on them by emphasizing their common uncertainties. I know that this conclusion will distress some of my friends whose ideas and judgement I respect. They considered me a serious-minded person, respectful of reason and mindful of scientific exactness. I hope that they will listen to the rest of my confession. As far as the conclusion of this book is concerned, I request the privilege of placing myself not "among those who are rash enough to believe they know, but among the wise men who know that they believe."[14]

Moreover, in expressing this opinion, I claim no special merit. Indeed, all my life I have remained faithful to the notion which inspired my first book, *Des Sciences physiques aux sciences*

[13] Sir James Jeans, *The Mysterious Universe*, 1930, p. 148.
[14] Rostand, op. cit., p. 13.

morales, which was first published in 1921. There I viewed scientific explanation not as a discovery of causes—which always escape us—but as a "creation of causes." This allows us to rediscover, by means of deductive reasoning, originating with verbal premises selected solely because of their explanatory capabilities, the equally verbal expression of perceptible appearances.

Perceptible appearances themselves depend upon the level on which they are observed. Causality is often no more than the by-product of the law of large numbers. Human phenomena observed on the level of the individual are unpredictable; they do not obey any strict laws until and unless they constitute phenomena physicists call "statistical" and economists call "macroscopic." Until we are better informed, and notwithstanding Louis de Broglie's current attempts to make the indeterminacy of particles the product of our ignorance rather than the result of an inherent indeterminacy analogous to that of animal or human behavior, I consider events in the world of "individuals" to be undetermined.

But my scepticism extends even further. Recent progress in physics, and especially the fundamental complementarity of the corpuscular and wave theories, have strengthened my belief that man's mind is inadequate as soon as it presumes to exceed the limits of the explanatory instruments made by and for itself. This inadequacy is revealed whenever science, following only its own logic, attempts to delve into the domain of fundamental causes. These have validity in the absolute, i.e. in a field external to man's mind. In other words, science ought to limit its ambition to the formal mathematics that can explain the appearances we know; it should not attempt to penetrate the world of essences, which is forever closed to us.

There is nothing in what we already know that can lead us to expect that once realities are no longer observed statistically, i.e. in a context of large numbers, they will be linked together in the universe as syllogisms are in our minds. It may be that the human mind is merely an analogy device, shaped over several hundreds of millions of years by the observation of the only reality that our senses enabled us to observe. In this reality causality rules unchallenged because it merely links appearances observed on our own level, that is to say, as statistical appearances.

A mind which knew about man only from actuarial tables would remain ignorant of the unpredictable outbursts of his creative liberty. On the other hand, if a man observed only individuals, on whatever level of organization, the same causes would never produce the same effects.

Thus I regard scientific explanation as simply a "creation of causes." It is intended to interpret a set of appearances that results as much from the size of the observer and the system of units he uses to express them as it does from the observed object itself.

Science is an *ad hoc* tool, valid only in the realm in which it was intended to provide explanation. It is a fact that it confers power, of course, because it makes explanation and prediction possible not only in the area from which it derives the general lessons it provides, but also in the neighboring areas, though there its abilities are less certain and more subject to revocation. But notwithstanding this feature, I do not believe that science exhausts reality.

I have no difficulty in admitting modes of knowledge outside science. These are valid and tend to "explain" other realms of perception which are no less real than scientific observation. Side by side with the mind of the scientist, I observe the minds of the poet, the musician, the painter, the philosopher. They too, in order to translate their specific "experiences," create systems of efficacious causes; by means of verse, music, painting, or philosophy, these experiences can be communicated to others, in whom they can arouse emotions similar to those from which they spring.

I recall Jean Cocteau's remark that realism is "the art of depicting accurately the goings on in the specific universe of the artist, without the slightest connection with what is usually called reality." I have no difficulty whatever in admitting that the mystic enraptured with love for the Creator whose presence he feels within himself—experiencing the certain, immediate, and total revelation of the supernatural world —adopts, in order to explain his vision, a system of particular causes which are different from those providing scientific explanation and enrapturing the mind of the scientist in his laboratory. Apart from but alongside perceptible appearances, I find that there are such things as love and faith, awareness of the infinite, the feeling of responsibility toward others and toward oneself, thirst for charity or prayer. All those feelings are no less real than hunger for positive knowledge and, again, confront us with the mystery of mysteries: the human person.

The last confession

I have, in fact, read this book while writing it, and I find that it has sharpened my beliefs on a certain number of points.

I believe:

that the entry of the "individual" into science, whether it be of matter, life, or man, is a revolution whose consequences had to be drawn;

that existence is always attained through the formation of societies, and that a creator, whether he is man or some other entity, is always an organizer of societies;

that "creation," because of its social nature, comprises successive levels of organization; individuals are societies for those of the next lower rank, and societies are individuals for those of next higher level.

I believe:

that the individual, which is the foundation of the universe, is wave and corpuscle, matter and spirit;

that it is a medium of behavior, the latter is a spontaneous outburst that responds to surrounding circumstances, not a passive presence indifferent to the external world;

that all behavior is the expression of psychism, which is merely a manner of existing—that is, a way of reacting to stimuli coming from the rest of the world;

that the complexity of psychism and especially the quantity of data that it can process depend upon its underlying neuronic or electronic equipment;

that psychism is the internal aspect and indeterminacy the external aspect of one and the same reality, which is that of the quanta of existence, known in the living world as individuals;

that the existence of persons is the great mystery of the universe and that it thrusts its roots into a subindividual medium, which is unique or manifold, but of which we know nothing.

I believe:

that the Promethean order which fills an ever-growing part of our universe is the result of thought which is reflected in things;

that, for this reason, it is not fortuitous but the product of a "creation";

that the techniques of this creation are elucidated by our various sciences, of matter as of man, and that these are always social sciences;

that creative thought is known to us when it is the thought of men;

that it has a direct influence on matter, but that its nature remains as mysterious to us as that of the person or entity from which it emanates;

that, for this reason, the problem of the kings is no easier to solve than the problem of the gods, but simply appears to be;

that both problems nevertheless shed light on one another by reason of their common uncertainties;

that the ambition of and justification for this book is its attempt to shed light on the techniques through which order is established and maintained in the universe;

that the unity of this book lies not in the subjects of its various chapters but in the structure of the knowledge which they express;

that this unity is the work of man's mind finding itself in things.

I hope:

that this book will stimulate accomplished scientists to go beyond the limits of their disciplines,

and that in this way, despite its obvious shortcomings, it will have contributed to the opening of the royal avenue leading toward the glory of a full synthesis of human knowledge.